You Can't Not Know

A Memoir about Medical School, Residency, and Life

By

Jack Spenser, M.D.

PREFACE

During my long career in medicine and pathology, I never had a mentor. I handed out applications, but nobody wanted the job.

It would have been nice, I think, to have had a mentor, someone who noticed how unique I was, discerned my special talents, and saw how deserving I was of extra care and attention. Never happened. No one noticed my special talents. There weren't any.

In the 1970s, when I trained, becoming a physician wasn't just a job, it was a calling, an adventure, a voyage to exotic places. I started medical school when I was twenty-one years old, bright and eager, a small sailboat in training, bouncing around in the harbor and channels, heading toward the open sea of medical practice, where I would sail away. A mentor could have explained the winds and the buoys – guided me through the channels, and pointed out the rocks so that I would not crash. No one did. The winds blew hard, and I crashed on plenty of rocks.

I started my pathology residency at Southeastern Medical Center, in Atlanta, after four years at Ivory Medical School at Dallas, which were undistinguished. The word the Ivory Medical School Faculty used about me was "solid."

During the first two years, my performances in the coursework – anatomy, biochemistry, physiology, pharmacology and every other subject – were deemed "solid." I showed up at all the lectures, did my lab work, and studied hard for the tests, and my grades were "solid." I was never one of the students who were called in for "counseling" (a euphemism for "shape up or you are out of here"), and I never had to go to summer school to repeat a subject. However, neither was I singled out for special praise.

The last two years of medical school, during my clinical rotations – surgery, pediatrics, internal medicine, orthopedics, and all the rest, I was told I did "solid work" – not great or outstanding work, just solid. Not that there was anything wrong with that. For example, the surgical interns and residents asked me to extend my emergency rotation for another two weeks, and then more weeks after that, so they could get some rest. About 10 p.m. they would sign some blank prescriptions for me to fill in as needed, go to bed, and get some much-needed sleep. While they were sleeping, they knew I could work on my own, late at night – dish out the antibiotics as needed, suture up the lacerations, take care of the burns, set or splint the broken bones, deliver the babies who couldn't make it to labor and delivery, and take care of anything else that came in. The surgical interns and residents woke up the next morning rested, relaxed, and confident that everything was under control. No one died, no one got sued, and no one ever got in trouble – because I was "solid."

However.

I wasn't chosen to be a member of AOA (Alpha Omega Alpha), the national medical honor society, nor did I win any awards. At my graduation ceremonies, others in my class won awards for best student in pediatrics, internal medicine, ob-gyn, surgery, and everything under the sun. It was hard to graduate without an award, but I managed to do so. Even the pathology department gave an award for best student, but my name was not called. That hurt, because I was the only student in my class who from the start wanted to be a pathologist. My classmates dreamed of becoming neurosurgeons, pediatricians, medical missionaries, heart surgeons, or something else glamourous and exciting. Not me. I just wanted to be a pathologist. I spent summers between school years in the pathology department, doing lab work and studying pathology. I took all the electives in pathology I could, even an externship my fourth year. Yet, somehow someone else won the pathology award.

Others in my class had mentors. One of my best friends, John McCurdie, late in his medical school career decided to go into pathology. He stayed at Ivory, encouraged to do so by Dr. Bruce Woolridge, our pathology teacher and a great hematopathologist. At

Ivory he went into hematopathology, just like his mentor, Dr. Woolridge. John was also active in teaching the pathology course under the guidance of Dr. Woolridge. In fact, John eventually took charge of the course, with the blessing of Dr. Woolridge. A very uplifting story.

Nothing like that ever happened to me.

Mack Puckett, my best friend during medical school and best man at my wedding, had a mentor, Dr. Ramsey, the chairman of the Urology Department. Dr. Ramsey had his eye on Mack, hoping that someday Mack would become a urologist. So when Mack graduated, Dr. Ramsey guided him to the prerequisite general surgery residency at Ivory. When Mack finished that, he had to fulfill his commitments to the Navy, and Dr. Ramsey followed Mack's progress there, letting him know that there would be a slot for him on the Ivory Urology house staff when he finished, which happened when Mack was in Pensacola, Florida. On the way to start his urology training, Mack stopped briefly in Atlanta to visit with me and my wife, Sarah. He told us how moved he was that Dr. Ramsey had waited all these years and saved a spot for him.

Yes, very moving.

In a larger arena, there are examples of physicians who acknowledge other physicians as mentors. As of this writing, the nation is battling the COVID-19 virus. The nation's "top infectious disease expert" helping to lead this fight is Dr. Anthony Fauci, head of the National Institute of Allergy and Infectious Diseases at the National Institute of Health, a very prestigious institution. He met his mentor, Dr. Sheldon Wolff, in the 1960s when Dr. Fauci was a fourth-year medical student. The two of them hit it off, and for the rest of Dr. Wolff's life, he served as a mentor to Dr. Fauci. Dr. Fauci describes Dr. Wolff as "the person who had the greatest impact on my career, a collaborator, best man at my wedding, my professional father, my mentor and closest friend." For his part, Dr. Wolff said about Dr. Fauci, "I can't remember a single moment when I was disappointed in him."

I can say with confidence that none of my teachers has ever said such a thing about me.

Nevertheless, when I graduated from Ivory Medical School, I matched at my first choice for internship and residency, Southeastern Medical Center. In my opinion, it was the best pathology department in the country, for me, mainly because of Dr. Darrell Hollis, who would be in charge of my training. I knew him mainly by reputation. When I interviewed for a position at Southeastern, I met Dr. Hollis briefly; I was very impressed by him, but I did not get the feeling he was very impressed by me. I'm not exactly sure how I was able to get one of the coveted Southeastern residency positions. It wasn't because of my grades, which were "solid" but not outstanding. I suspect my letters of recommendation were positive, although they couldn't have been *that* helpful. My high scores on the National Boards must have helped; they were excellent in every subject, including pathology. But then everyone in my class at Ivory Medical School had high scores – the highest scores in the country when I was there. I put Southeastern down as my first choice to match, with Ivory as my second choice. I matched at Southeastern. Dr. Hollis was going to be my teacher.

I am unaware of any books detailing mentor-student relationships between physicians, although my observation is that they are quite common.

Writers, on the other hand, are more apt to describe how other writers, older writers, became mentors. A good example is a book by Tom Grimes aptly named *Mentor: A Memoir*, which describes his teacher, Frank Conroy, who believed in Grimes and supported him during the periods of rejection that he experienced early in his career. To paraphrase the book jacket, it describes how an older more experienced master can nourish and build the talents of a younger student.

This is not that kind of book.

However, I am not alone, I think, in lacking a mentor. Perhaps many of my readers have been left out of that experience as well. But I suspect *all* of my readers at some time in their lives have had a great teacher, or at least a *best* teacher. Had to.

So this book is not about a mentor, but it is about a great teacher, Dr. Darrell Hollis, a teacher of pathology, who was the best teacher I ever had. I describe how he changed my life, whether he wanted to or not, and how that relationship changed over time. It is about how we seek guidance when we are young, and look for answers from older and more experienced individuals who hopefully can pass on their knowledge and wisdom to us, so we can get rid of the horrible uncertainty in life.

This story takes place at a large charity hospital in the 1970s, a place for training medical students and residents. To paraphrase Dickens, it was the worst of times and the best of times:

It was the worst of times: The drugs we used weren't as potent. The exponential advances in radiology, like CAT scans and MRIs, hadn't occurred. Medicine as practiced now is to 1970s as 1970s medicine was to World War II medicine. The scientific and technological advances that have occurred since my training would have been deemed science fiction at the time, but they happened.

It was the best of times: Being a physician when I trained was a privilege not a job. We were proud to be physicians and physicians in training. Physicians had power and autonomy and weren't the corporate Twinkies they are now. The American Medical Association was the most powerful union in the world. Now, it's a joke. Physicians and patients made decisions for their patients. Now insurance companies or other health care entities control what happens. I could expand on this theme, but I am sure virtually every one of my readers has experienced what I am talking about.

In summary, I learned to be a physician/pathologist during a simpler time, but it was not a gentler time. In fact, it's a miracle I survived.

CHAPTER 1

I was terrified of the man, Dr. Darrell Hollis. He was in his mid-forties, tall and lanky like a split end, which he had been in Division One Football at Georgia Tech. He was still fit, about six feet two, 180 lbs, all muscle and grit. He kind of loped as he walked. He looked like a marine drill sergeant – the hair of his eyebrows was longer than the hair on his head. His pale blue eyes looked through large refractive glasses with metallic silver rims; he wanted to SEE. He stood ramrod straight, with a knowing look on his face and a perpetual frown, as he perceived the many shortcomings of his students and pathology house staff. He was always the "smartest guy in the room." He was the smartest person I ever met.

It was late summer in the South at Southeastern Medical Center, a charity hospital and a teaching hospital. Layne Siler and I were pathology interns (first-year residents). We had been on the autopsy service of the pathology department for only three weeks.

We were in the morgue/autopsy suite located in the basement of the hospital. As you entered the area, there was a little smell, but not that bad, kind of a clinical smell, the kind that you detect when you go to a doctor's office for a sore throat or something. Anytime you're around sick patients, there's a smell. In the autopsy suite the patients are plenty sick. They're dead.

Visually, think bright lights and shiny surfaces. Overhead fluorescent lights illuminated white walls above stainless-steel countertops, with metal drawers underneath. The metal drawers contained power saws, dissecting tools, and other equipment. These counters surrounded a black and white tile floor under three stainless-steel tables, each large enough to accommodate a dead body. No bodies were around. Instead, on top of one of the tables I had placed a large metal pan next to a cork dissecting board. The metal pan contained the organs of a deceased patient. The dissecting board was partially covered with dissecting instruments – scissors, scalpel, and forceps. The table tilted, so hoses could spray water, which went through small perforations in the metal to a catch basin and drain to a sink. The place was very clean and antiseptic.

Layne Siler and I were standing on one side of the table, and Dr. Hollis towered over us on the other side. Layne was not particularly tall, and I am shorter than Layne. Layne was a little older than me. He liked to fish and was an excellent runner. Years later he would run the Boston Marathon.

Dr. Hollis was dressed as he was always dressed, conservative – starched white lab coat, white shirt, and a solid-colored crisply knotted tie, dark pants – all put together with Prussian precision. A couple of ballpoint pens and mechanical pencils were tucked into the lab coat pocket, along with a retractable metallic pointer, which he could use for slide presentations or to point something out in a tissue specimen. He wore a metal watch on his left wrist and a wedding band on his left ring finger. Layne and I wore gray surgical scrubs. All three of us wore white plastic aprons hanging around our necks and tied behind our backs. Latex gloves covered our hands and lower wrists. I was presenting my autopsy findings to Dr. Hollis. Layne and I were still new and scared.

The metal pan was to Dr. Hollis's right, and the cork dissecting board was directly in front of him. One by one, Dr. Hollis took the organs out of the pan, placed them on the board, quizzed me and Layne about them, and then placed the organs to his left, gently hosing everything off with water from time to time.

The review was about over. Dr. Hollis had taken the last organ out of the pan, the heart. As usual he had saved the most important organ for last. He proceeded to examine it carefully. The heart is a reddish pink globoid muscle, a little bigger than a closed fist of a large hand, weighing about three-quarters of a pound, incredibly powerful, a four-chambered blood-driving pump sending blood to the whole body. Dr. Hollis examined the heart's four chambers and the valves separating them in the order in which blood flowed – right atrium, tricuspid valve, right ventricle to pulmonary arteries, pulmonary veins to left atrium, and mitral valve to left ventricle.

Every structure was normal, until he reached the mitral valve, between the left atrium and left ventricle. It was definitely not normal.

"What is your diagnosis of the mitral valve?" asked Dr. Hollis, in his baritone voice, with a drawl, like a western cowboy.

"Rheumatic valvar disease," I answered.

"How did you arrive at such a ludicrous diagnosis?"

It wasn't difficult. The mitral valve has two leaflets, like two wings of a large butterfly, held onto the muscle wall of the heart by delicate strands like the cords of a trampoline, called chordae tendineae. As pressure in the left atrium builds, blood forces the leaflets open, like a trapdoor. The trapdoor closes from pressure, which builds as the left ventricle pumps blood to the aorta.

But the mitral valve in this deceased patient did not look anything like that. In medical jargon, it was shot to hell. The mitral valve leaflets were not like butterfly wings, but like a crusty rusty anchor with barnacles, because they were scarred and calcified. The chordae tendineae, which held the leaflets of the mitral valve in place, were not long, thin, and delicate – but were shortened and thickened by white scar tissue and looked like thick crusty rubber bands that no longer worked. I pointed all this out as well as the new blood vessels on the valve, where they were not supposed to be, a futile attempt to try to heal the valve, and very typical of rheumatic valvular disease. The mitral valve was very diseased secondary to a bout of rheumatic fever, so diseased that it killed the patient, a sixty-five-year-old woman. With the delicate anatomy of the mitral valve so disrupted, it did not work as a finely crafted valve for the piston of the heart, but like a rusty creaky valve in a V8 1951 Ford, creaking and leaking oil. Instead of leaking oil, the mitral valve leaked blood, sending it back from the left ventricle into the left atrium. I delivered this erudite, concise, and succinct description and diagnosis to Dr. Hollis, and I was quite pleased with myself. I had studied hard and it showed.

Dr. Hollis said, "Very interesting, and possibly relevant, but you have missed the most significant lesion. Perhaps you may wish to re-examine this heart?"

I did so. I looked and looked. "I don't see anything I missed," I said.

"You look, but you do not see," said Dr. Hollis.

I tried to "see," but without success. "I don't know what I missed."

"Incredible incompetence," said Dr. Hollis. "How can you sleep at night knowing so little? You can't not know!"

Dr. Hollis turned to Layne. "What did the incompetent Dr. Spenser miss?"

Layne looked at the heart carefully for a few minutes, but then gave up. "I'm afraid I am just as incompetent as Dr. Spenser, because I don't see anything he missed."

Dr. Hollis said, "You can't be as incompetent as Dr. Spenser. Dr. Spenser is the *pinnacle* of incompetence."

Think of it! The definition of pinnacle is "the most successful point, the culmination." For me to be the pinnacle of incompetence, the most incompetent intern/resident/student Dr. Hollis had ever encountered, out of thousands of such individuals he had taught, well, it's breathtaking. And think of all the incompetence in the world, all the incompetence Dr. Hollis had seen – and I was the pinnacle of all that as well, the most successful at incompetence ever existing in time. What an achievement! Finally, at the relatively advanced age of twenty-five years old, I was the absolute best at something. I might not have been the best tennis player on my high school or college teams, and I might not have been valedictorian of my high school class, and I didn't graduate from college summa cum laude, and I was far from first in my medical school class – but according to no less an authority than Dr. Hollis, I was the pinnacle, the best, the most successful ever – at incompetence.

What Layne and I had missed were MacCallum's plaques, which are zones of scarring on the inner surface of the left atrium, which were secondary to the backflow of blood from the left ventricle to the left atrium. The resultant turbulence and mechanical forces caused irritation and injury to the lining of the left ventricle, hence the scarring. Even when Dr. Hollis pointed to the plaques, they were hard to see – pale, as subtle as the mirror image of a ghost.

Dr. Hollis said, "They were first described by Dr. William George MacCallum, American pathologist, born 1874, died 1944, and are named after him. This lesion is the most significant lesion because it demonstrates loss of function of the heart, which is more important than some interesting anatomical changes. The loss of function led to this patient's death."

I never missed MacCallum's plaques again, and I am sure neither did Layne – which was the point of what Dr. Hollis said and did.

Layne and I shared an office. During the rest of the day, each of the second-, third-, and fourth-year residents stopped by and asked us what in the world had happened during the morning autopsy review, because they had never seen Dr. Hollis so upset, and they wondered what in the world the two of us had done to provoke him so. No doubt they did this in a spirit of compassion to help two struggling interns.

CHAPTER 2

Southeastern University School of Medicine is a legendary place in the South. Much of the campus was built in the 1930s with red brick.

The steps on the stairs between the floors have indentations a couple of inches deep, marking where generations of students walked (or ran) up and down. No one knows what the elevators look like, because no one has time to wait for elevators. Class pictures of every class ever to graduate from Southeastern, and pictures of all the house staff ever to rotate through the institution line the hallways. Portraits of some famous graduates hang in lecture halls, because they have gone on to become national and international celebrities; two have won Nobel Prizes in medicine.

The hospital and medical school surround a central courtyard in which a sidewalk separates a grass lawn, with dark brick walls on each side. The walls and trees provide shadows, which gradually move throughout the day. Vertical windows are interspersed in the walls. The windows tend to be open during pleasant weather in the spring and fall.

At one end of the courtyard is the main entrance to the medical school, which is magnificent. A huge dark brown oak door is flanked by floor-to-ceiling glass windows, under an archway of gray concrete with an engraved black arc carved into the cement. To me the art depicts a sunrise or knowledge spreading outward and upward, above which is the inscription SOUTHEASTERN MEDICAL SCHOOL.

The overall effect is that of a British college like the University of Oxford, something out of *Brideshead Revisited.*

Does all this impress a twenty-five-year-old pathology intern? You'd better believe it.

CHAPTER 3

Dr. Hollis wrote a textbook of pathology, which unsurprisingly was the textbook he used to teach the pathology course to second-year medical students. It was THE BOOK at Southeastern, but to my knowledge was not used as a textbook for pathology anywhere else in the country. I certainly hadn't used it at Ivory, which put me behind at Southeastern. All my fellow interns had gone to school at Southeastern and therefore had learned THE BOOK and had a head start. I had to learn it quickly for two reasons:

1. I had to be able to answer Dr. Hollis's questions, and the correct answers were in THE BOOK.

2. Part of my job was to help teach pathology to the second-year medical students, so I had to be familiar with THE BOOK to do this.

THE BOOK had twenty-one chapters, well thought out and well written. I wish I HAD used this textbook because it was really good. The book reflected Dr. Hollis's mind, organized and thorough. The first nine chapters covered general disease processes. The remaining chapters each covered the various organ systems of the body – respiratory system, cardiovascular system, genitourinary system and so forth.

Before the start of the fall semester, some of the second-year medical students were congregated around the medical school bookstore. As Dr. Hollis walked by, he was recognized by the students.

"Dr. Hollis," one of them asked, "do we have to buy your textbook to pass the course?"

"Son," he replied, "you have to buy that textbook to get *in* the course."

CHAPTER 4

The hierarchy of the Department of Pathology was simple. At the bottom were the four interns/first-year residents – Layne Siler, Fred Adams, Sid Steinberg, and me. Layne had gone to medical school at Southeastern. After graduating, he did an internal medicine internship at Charity Hospital in New Orleans and hated it. I overheard a conversation between Layne and Dr. Hollis about why Layne had left internal medicine to go into pathology. Dr. Hollis was always suspicious of such transfers. He didn't want residents who left a clinical specialty like internal medicine or surgery because it was too tough, and wanted to go into pathology because it was easier; it wasn't. The conversation went something like this:

Layne: You really want to know why I left internal medicine to do pathology?

Dr. Hollis: Yeah.

Layne: Because internal medicine didn't make any sense to me. We would give patient steroids for some disease, or a certain antibiotic for a certain infection, and no one could tell me why. There was no scientific explanation for why steroids worked sometimes, and sometimes they didn't. Or why antibiotics worked or didn't work. There was little that was scientific about it. We treated the patients with a certain algorithm, because it had always been done that way; maybe there was some logic to what was done, but a lot of the time there wasn't – it just seemed to work, God knows how. I wanted to do something scientific that makes sense, like pathology.

Years later, Dr. Hollis told me that he regarded this explanation as a perfectly good reason to go into pathology.

Fred Adams had also gone to medical school at Southeastern after graduating from Emory University. He was tall, blond, and very well organized. In high school in Georgia he had won championships with the debate team, which meant he was used to writing summaries of articles on index cards and filing them for future reference. Now he applied these techniques to pathology articles. That sort of approach to all things pathology was very successful, and I envied him for how disciplined he was with his time and energy.

The remaining intern/resident was Sid Steinberg, who became my best friend during my residency. The two of us hit it off. From time to time my wife, Sarah, and I double-dated with Sid and his girlfriend, who would go on to become his fiancée and then his wife. Sid told me I would have been one of the groomsmen at the wedding, but the scheduled date of the birth of my first son was almost the same time as the date of the wedding. Sid was understandably worried that there would be a conflict, so he held off on making me one of his groomsmen. Sarah and I were able to attend the wedding, which was a lot of fun. Sid was very smart. He attended medical school at Southeastern after graduating from the University of Chicago. He had a mustache and a professorial air about him, verging on arrogant, which bothered some people but didn't bother me at all. If you can do it, it ain't bragging.

But, honestly, all of my fellow interns were smart. Not only that, but they had all gone to medical school at Southeastern. Dr. Hollis had been their pathology teacher. They had used Dr. Hollis's textbook. Compared to me, the three of them had a big head start.

Four second-year residents, three third-year residents, and three fourth-year residents ahead of us completed the house staff level of the hierarchy.

The next rank up was the faculty, which was in charge of our training and everything else in the department. There were two divisions of pathology to cover:

1. The division of Anatomic Pathology, which included autopsy pathology and surgical pathology. Dr. Hollis was the dominant force in this division. He was in charge of the au-

topsy service. He was also in charge of the pathology course for second-year medical students and was the overall director of the pathology residency program. We had various attendings in charge of surgical pathology and the various subspecialties of surgical pathology – dermatopathology, hematopathology, cardiovascular pathology, neuropathology, renal pathology, liver pathology and so forth. A pediatric pathologist supervised our pathology rotation at the children's hospital.

2. The division of Clinical Pathology included chemistry, microbiology, hematology, and blood banking. Each of these services had a laboratory director in charge of teaching these disciplines.

Finally, at the top, Dr. Page was the chairman of the department.

CHAPTER 5

My residency rotations, with predicted difficulty, went like this from beginning to end:

1. Six months autopsy rotation with Dr. Hollis. Tough start.

2. Three months chemistry. Easy.

3. Six months surgical pathology. Busy and hard but not as tough as the autopsy service with Dr. Hollis.

4. Three months hematology. Easy.

5. Three months surgical pathology at the Veterans Administration Hospital (VA). Busy and hard, but not as tough as the autopsy service with Dr. Hollis.

6. Three months blood banking. Easy.

7. Three months microbiology. Easy.

8. Three months pediatric pathology at the Children's Hospital – surgical pathology and autopsy pathology, as well as some clinical pathology. Busy and hard, but not as tough as the autopsy service with Dr. Hollis.

9. Another three months autopsy rotation with Dr. Hollis. The last hurdle.

10. Three months liver/kidney/skin pathology rotation. Easy.

11. Three months hematology. Easy.

12. Three months chemistry. Easy.

13. Three months microbiology. Easy.

14. Three months blood banking. Easy.

There was not much training in cytopathology, the science of trying to make diagnoses based on cellular specimens rather than tissue specimens. I did get exposed to some cytopathology during my surgical pathology rotations, but that was about it. The art of sticking a needle into an organ (e.g., lung, liver, or pancreas), aspirating some cells, looking at them under the microscope, and making diagnoses was just getting started when I was at Southeastern. Some of the old-fashioned pathologists like Dr. Hollis were skeptical of this new discipline. We had this conversation:

Me: I think I need to get better at cytopathology.

Dr. Hollis: You know what a malignant cell looks like, don't you?

Me: Yeah, I think I know what a malignant cell looks like.

Dr. Hollis: That's all you need to know about cytopathology.

In summary, the clinical pathology rotations (chemistry, hematology, microbiology, and blood banking) totaled twenty-four months, and the anatomic pathology rotations (surgical pathology and autopsy pathology and everything else) totaled twenty-four months – four years of training. When I finished, I would be eligible to take the examinations to be board certified in anatomic and clinical pathology. The pass rate for the time I took the tests was about 50%. However, no one from Southeastern had ever flunked.

So the prognosis for me to be a board-certified pathologist was pretty good if I could make it through the forty-eight months of training. Unfortunately, I wasn't sure I could survive the first six months, the autopsy rotation with Dr. Hollis, which was the most challenging and difficult part of the program, by far.

Layne Siler was with me the first three months on the autopsy service, just the two of us. Then he rotated off, and Sid Steinberg took his place for a three-month rotation with me. So I had a total of six straight months with one other guy, first Layne and then Sid. The remaining intern, Fred Adams, wasn't on the autopsy rotation at all the first six months. His autopsy rotations would take place later in his residency.

So my residency was front-loaded: I started with the toughest rotation, with Dr. Hollis. I guess that someone had to get the work done those first six months and do those autopsies. It was interesting, though, that not only did I start out on the autopsy service as an intern for three months, but I stayed on for another three months while others came and went, or didn't come at all. I'm sure it was a coincidence that the schedule worked out that way, that out of all the interns, I had the most challenging first year. I was never suspicious that this was some kind of initiation for the one intern who came from another medical school. Never.

CHAPTER 6

Part of my job was to assist with the teaching of the laboratory part of the pathology course given to the second-year medical students. The formal teaching lectures were done by Dr. Hollis and the rest of the faculty. Whenever possible, I attended the lectures given by Dr. Hollis.

The lecture halls had tiered seating, five levels. Each tier had a line of old-fashioned desks, the kind with a chair that automatically folds up when not in use, with a writing surface and an armrest on the side, which could slide up when it was time to take notes.

The students wore long white lab coats; the young men wore collared shirts with a tie, and the young women wore dresses. A student improperly dressed (e.g., without a tie) would be asked to leave. A student coming in late would be peppered by difficult questions from Dr. Hollis about the subject to be covered, something like "What is the most important thing to know about necrosis?" Then Dr. Hollis would go back to the beginning of the lecture and start again. A tardy student was a rarity.

Dr. Hollis took his place at the front of the class at 8 a.m. sharp or a little earlier. He stood at a podium on a stage a little elevated above the floor, a screen and blackboard behind him. He usually projected Kodachrome slides on the screen. The Kodachromes tended to be pictures of organs with various disease processes, or photomicrographs of the microscopic findings. As the slides were projected, Dr. Hollis would discuss the various disease processes as they were visually demonstrated. He frequently called on the members of the class and asked questions in a Socratic manner.

A lecture early in the course covered edema, a condition in which tissues are swollen by fluid for one reason or another. Dr. Hollis began his lecture by saying, "Okay, to start off with, I want all of you who wake up in the morning with edema of the scrotum to raise your hand."

One of the female students raised her hand. Then a few more students did as well, but only the ladies. Incredulous, Dr. Hollis said, "You all wake up with edema of the scrotum?" They all nodded yes. The lecture continued.

CHAPTER 7

As I describe the procedures for doing an autopsy, and the review process, my readers may reasonably ask: How can you DO that?

A reasonable question. For much of the history of mankind, examining a dead body was taboo. Leonardo da Vinci was the first person to study anatomy by actually doing dissections of cadavers, but that didn't happen until about 1490; we don't know the exact date because initially he did these studies surreptitiously. He ended up doing about thirty dissections. Until then anatomy was largely learned by external examination.

Autopsies to formally study disease came much later. Chinese societies practiced ancestor veneration, and autopsies were forbidden. Some religions forbid dissection of the dead. It wasn't until 1876 that autopsies became part of medicine and science, when the Prussian pathologist Rudolph Virchow published his treatise on autopsy techniques – less than one hundred years before I started my autopsy rotation.

The lack of autopsies was one of the many things that kept medicine from progressing and being more effective. Over the course of medical history, it is astonishing how ineffective physicians have been until recently. For 2500 years, until the early 1800s, the most common medical therapy was bleeding a patient, which might have helped a few plethoric hypertensive patients, but harmed many more. As Sir Gilbert Blane (1749–1834) said in *Elements of Medical Logick* "…there is a wide difference between a good physician and a bad one, but a small difference between a good physician and no physician at all." That was probably generous to physicians. In fact, a case can be made that up to the time antibiotics were discovered in the late 1930s, a visit to the doctor was more likely to harm a patient than help a patient.

Scientific studies, including autopsies, would have improved medical care.

If Hamlet had available to him a good autopsy service to examine his dead father, he could have avoided all kinds of suspicion, indecision, and sorrow. Of course, that would have ruined the plot of one of Shakespeare's greatest works, but art follows the culture and society where it arises: Shakespeare's great play artistically describes what can happen when medical facts are not known, and the grief it can cause. "Artistically describes!?" What an understatement! William Shakespeare was the greatest writer who ever lived. No one else comes close.

At least two demands can be placed on a corpse:

1. The appearance of a well-preserved body may console and support grieving family and friends.

2. However, that body can also leave footprints of what happened and why, and a careful postmortem examination can give knowledge to the doctors taking care of the patient during life, and also comfort the family. The postmortem findings can also advance medical and scientific knowledge.

In my experience, both demands can be met. To my knowledge, none of the postmortem exams I have done hindered the professionals at a funeral home in accomplishing this goal of making the body of the deceased as presentable as it would have been with no postmortem exam. The clinicians and/or the families of the deceased have always been interested in the autopsy findings, and some of these discoveries I have written up and published in medical journals.

My experience was that my postmortem studies almost always helped the clinicians who took care of the patient. They were better able to understand what had happened, and it hopefully led to improvements in their diagnostic and treatment abilities. Three times I learned things from postmortem exams that I went on to describe and publish in scientific journals, adding negligible, but hopefully helpful bits of scientific knowledge to the medical literature. Sometimes, what I learned by doing an autopsy was additional information that answered questions from the family, and explaining what had happened to the deceased was comforting to them.

You are avoiding the question, Dr. Spenser, so again, how can you DO such a thing as an autopsy?

Answering that question is delicate and tricky, and I am sure different pathologists would answer the question different ways. Here is my answer:

I believe that the dead body I am examining is not that person, but only a body. The life force is gone. I believe that a human being has a body and a soul; when death happens, the soul goes, the essence of the person is gone, and only the body remains. Body and soul are separate. When I am doing an autopsy, I have no sense whatsoever of the person, the soul, or the essence of the patient associated with that body. It's gone.

The body that remains should be treated with reverence and respect.

But:

The eyes are lackluster with no sparkle; the "windows to the soul" are boarded up.

There is no change in body posture, no body language – only silence.

The heart has no "heartfelt" feelings.

The brain has no thoughts, no conscience, no beliefs, no memory, no mystery, and no soul. It's just a brain.

The soul is gone, and only the body remains. "Where did the soul go?" you ask with a smile. And I say, with a smile, "I don't know."

But having come this far, why stop now? I am a Christian (see John 3:16). I also believe in karma, that the good and bad you do come back to you in this life or the next.

Which is as far as I dare to tread in this treacherous philosophical territory, the dreaded mind-body problem. I obviously fall in the dualism camp, but I end up there not with logic, but based on observations of bodies, associated organs, and tissues. The soul and body are separate.

For a more lighthearted approach to this issue, I recommend *the Mind-Body Problem*, a book of fiction by Rebecca Goldstein.

That's enough, I think. A further exploration of this issue would result in a different kind of book. As it is, this chapter is more serious than I want this book to be, but I needed to make this explanation so you can know how I coped with examining bodies, tissues, and organs of patients. Now I hope you enjoy the stories.

For our part, we pathology residents studied bodies, organs, and tissues to learn pathology, because, well, we had to. Eventually, our training would end, and we would all go on to be practicing pathologists and have to make diagnoses on specimens from real live patients who were sick and wanted to know why they were sick – the patients and their doctors would want diagnoses from us, practicing pathologists. And the diagnoses had to be right, because the stakes could be quite high, literally life and death. We took our training very seriously; it was what we were called to do.

CHAPTER 8

Why was the autopsy rotation with Dr. Hollis so tough? An autopsy itself can't be that hard to do. You make some incisions, retrieve the organs, dissect them, and make some diagnoses – no big deal. Obviously it takes some training and practice, but it's not like there are any really high stakes here: the patient's already dead. If you make a mistake, the patient's not going to have any complications to weigh on your conscience, and the patient or patient's family are not going to sue you; convincing a judge or jury that a negligent autopsy caused pain, suffering, loss of consortium, or anything else would be very difficult – the patient was deceased before you arrived on the scene.

A surgery resident, on the other hand, has all kinds of pressure while doing an operation: a mistake can lead to bleeding, infection, paralysis, and innumerable other complications, including death.

A pediatric resident or internal medicine resident has similar pressures. When treating diabetic ketoacidosis or sepsis or some other disease, the medications, doses, and treatment details have to be correct – otherwise the patient dies.

I never had that kind of pressure doing an autopsy. However, with Dr. Hollis directing the service, there was a lot of pressure to do the job right, and that took a lot of work. To illustrate how and why, here's how my first autopsy went.

It was August, in the South, and this first autopsy on my own as an intern was relatively easy as autopsies go. The deceased patient was in her fifties, lived in a wood house without air-conditioning, and one hot day she suffered a heat stroke while sitting on her front porch. She came to the emergency room with a temperature of 110 degrees, comatose. She was resuscitated, but died a few days later after a brief hospital stay. An interesting aspect of her clinical course was that she had rhabdomyolysis, a condition in which skeletal muscle breaks down rapidly – just kind of dissolves – and ends up in the blood with deleterious consequences. The rhabdomyolysis was probably caused by the excess body heat. In the 1970s rhabdomyolysis was not a well-known complication of heat stroke, so when the patient died, the clinicians who took care of her wanted an autopsy done to learn more about rhabdomyolysis and heat stroke.

First, I had to look at the autopsy consent permit and make sure it was legal for me to proceed. You would think that this would be straightforward. Wrong. There was only one "owner" of the body of the deceased, and by law that person was the next of kin. So one person, and one person only, had the right to consent to an autopsy. Unfortunately, finding that person and getting consent, was frequently challenging. For example, for a married patient the next of kin was the spouse. Therefore, the spouse, and only the spouse, had the power to grant permission for an autopsy. The problem was that at this charity hospital, a lot of times the spouse wasn't around to sign; a fair number of husbands (and wives) had simply split, leaving behind a spouse with children, but hadn't bothered to go through the hassle, time, and expense of a divorce. The spouse was alive, but gone, sometimes on the run from the law, so the last thing that "next of kin" cared about was signing an autopsy permit. Also, this was before social media, cell phones, e-mail and all the other communication aids we have now. Sometimes we depended on telegrams. So I can't tell you how many times I got an autopsy permit signed by one of the grown children, but not the absent spouse, which unfortunately was not a valid permit. I spent countless hours relating these facts to busy overwhelmed clinical residents, that I needed a valid permit before I could proceed. I would hear every excuse in the book – the "family wants the autopsy," how hard it was to find the next of kin who had moved to the other end of the country, and how incredibly selfish and lazy I was not to do the autopsy with the paperwork I had. However, an invalid permit was not a technicality. Pathologists have gone to jail for battery for doing unauthorized autopsies.

I had a valid permit for this heat stroke patient. But I wasn't done with the paperwork. Before I did the autopsy, I had to review the medical chart so I knew what to expect and what to do. In this case, for example, it was imperative that I collect samples of skeletal muscle – calf muscles, hamstrings, muscle in the arm, etc. – to study the rhabdomyolysis, which is usually NOT done in a routine autopsy. In this autopsy it was arguably the most important task.

Which brings up a point: every autopsy was different.

Then, finally, it was time to actually do the autopsy. The morgue assistant (diener) carefully tied off the vessels to the neck and extremities so the embalmer could find them and do his job. Then the trick of the thing was for us to remove the organs en bloc. When the diener (morgue assistant) and I were finished, we sewed everything back together and released the body to the funeral home. The professional staff at the funeral home would take over, and when they were finished, there would be no way to tell a postmortem exam had been done. In my career I have had countless interactions with funeral home professionals, and I totally respect the work they do, which is to handle death with dignity. Never in my career has there ever been any kind of unpleasant interaction with the family and friends of the deceased, or the funeral home staff, about an autopsy I did or anything else.

I proceeded with the meticulous dissection of the removed organs. I weighed each organ and placed tissue samples in a large bottle of formalin for fixation, the first step to preparing microscopic slides. With experience and training, it takes about four hours to do an autopsy from start to finish. This first autopsy I did for Dr. Hollis took me six hours to do.

Of course, there was more to doing an autopsy than just going through the motions and doing the work. From first incision to last organ examined, I had to look and SEE the lesions and the pathology. If I missed anything, I knew that Dr. Hollis would point it out to me, not in a nice way. When I was finished with the dissection, I put the organs in a metal pan, which I placed on a shelf of the walk-in refrigerator, where it would stay until the review with Dr. Hollis the next morning.

Then I went back to my office to get ready to make the clinical presentation to Dr. Hollis the next morning. That actually took some time, because Dr. Hollis did not like the usual way medical charts were organized. At that time, before electronic medical records, the front of the chart started with the present illness and THEN documented the past medical history in a haphazard manner, like flashbacks. The medical chart of a deceased person was like the movie *Citizen Kane*, in which the protagonist dies at the beginning, and then the remainder of the film tells the story of his life.

That was not what Dr. Hollis wanted to hear.

Dr. Hollis wanted to hear the story from the beginning, starting way back with the patient's first interaction with Southeastern Medical Center, and then every medical event up to the last admission. Then he wanted to hear what led to the final admission to Southeastern and the hospital course of that last admission, day by day if possible, with all pertinent lab results and X-ray findings. Dr. Hollis was less interested in esoteric tests on the patient than in simple observations about the patient's condition – was the patient alert, comatose, stuporous, obtunded...? At the conclusion of the presentation, Dr. Hollis wanted a description of the events that had happened around the time of death.

This way of presenting the patient meant that I couldn't just bring the medical chart to the autopsy review and "wing it." I had to put the facts in the order Dr. Hollis wanted to hear them. There were "war stories" about residents who hadn't put in the time and energy to present the cases correctly. Here are a couple of verified quotes of what Dr. Hollis said:

1. "This is the worst presentation of a patient I have ever heard."

2. "I have never heard a more inept, ill-prepared presentation. I am very disappointed."

By the time I had the clinical findings and clinical course ready to present, it was dark outside. I phoned Dr. Hollis at home to tell him what I thought had happened to the patient so he could read up on the topic and be ready to review the case with me and Layne (and anybody else who showed up) the next morning at 7 a.m. sharp. I slid a paper with my handwritten **Preliminary Anatomic Diagnoses** under the door to Dr. Hollis's office. As soon as that was done, I was "locked in" with my impressions.

I spent the rest of the evening and most of the night learning about heat stroke. I got no sleep. I read as much as humanly possible about heat stroke. Some of it was quite interesting and scary. Some of the research had been done on military recruits, who were subjected to high environmental temperatures, hooked up to various monitors, and those results recorded – body temperature, blood pressure, pulse, respirations and so forth, with blood drawn from time to time to check metabolic changes. The poor soldiers suffered from heat stroke, with a real risk of death in some cases.

I had my own risks the next morning, at 7 a.m. sharp.

But first, another war story:

Prior to my arrival at Southeastern, a resident we will call Dr. Stooge didn't make it to the autopsy review at 7 a.m. for some reason or another. He was the resident in the "line of fire" that morning, but he wasn't there. Of course Dr. Hollis was there on time, actually a few minutes early. The clock registered 7 a.m. and no Dr. Stooge. As always, there was a fair amount of tension before the autopsy review with Dr. Hollis, but the anxiety went up off the charts when Dr. Stooge did not show up. Finally, shortly after 7 a.m., Dr. Stooge raced into the morgue, papers flying, hair messed up, and he took his place at the review. Dr. Hollis glared at him and said, "It's the LATE Dr. Stooge."

He replied, "According to Greenwich Mean Time, it's 7 a.m. sharp."

"According to Darrell Hollis Mean Time, it's 7:06 a.m. You're late."

We started on time. There were three of us. As usual, Layne and I were seated on one side of the autopsy table, and Dr. Hollis was seated on the other side of the table. The agenda was always the same: The resident who did the autopsy presented the clinical information, which of course ended with the death of the patient.

Dr. Hollis asked, "What were the clinical impressions?" These were the diagnoses and impressions of the internists taking care of the patient. Of course the answer was heat stroke.

Dr. Hollis then asked, "What are your impressions of the case?" which he already knew, having read my Preliminary Anatomic Diagnoses slid under the door to his office. Of course my answer was heat stroke.

A series of questions and answers followed, which went something like this:

"What are the sources of heat to the body?" asked Dr. Hollis.

"Radiation," I answered.

"What kind of radiation?"

"Sunlight. When the sun shines down on me, I feel hot. In the shade I feel cooler."

"You think this patient died of excessive sunlight?"

"No, but there is heat in the atmosphere, especially around here in August. Metabolism of the body also generates heat."

"What kind of metabolism?"

A long question and answer session of biochemical reactions followed.

"How does the body get rid of heat?" Dr. Hollis asked.

"Peripheral circulation, the warm body heat from the blood goes into the air, but when it's hot, that's not effective, so the body sweats."

The follow-up questions and answers were about sweat glands – anatomy, physiology, and biochemistry. We talked about how there are three million sweat glands in the body, which can sweat up to about six pounds of water in an hour. As that sweat evaporates, the body cools down.

"How does heat stroke happen?" asked Dr. Hollis.

"That's a good question. I don't think anyone knows."

"All my questions are good. It's the answers that are so bad."

"Well, *I* don't know."

"You can't not know."

I decided to wing it. "The patient's body heats up, and then the sweating can't keep up enough to cool the body down, maybe secondary to dehydration – the sweat glands don't have enough fluid to work with, so the patient's temperature keeps going up and up, until it reaches 110 degrees or so, which is incompatible with life. You get bad things happening, like what happened with this patient, rhabdomyolysis."

"Can you think of any factors that might have predisposed this patient to heat stroke?"

I couldn't think of any. I said, "No, the patient was not that old. She was in good health, no heart or lung diseases, and no chronic diseases. She had not been exerting herself, doing any physical exercise. She was just sitting on the front porch of her un-air-conditioned house. I can't think of anything that would have predisposed her to heat stroke."

"You said she was obese?"

"Very."

"Do you think a layer of thick fat around her body could have acted as insulation, like wearing a fur coat, keeping in heat and predisposing her to heat stroke?"

"Yeah. That's really good. Why didn't I think of that?"

"Why indeed."

We got into how the temperature of the body is regulated by the thalamus, why body temp goes up during an infection (the infection causes chemicals called pyrogens to be released, which go to the thalamus, which sends out signals to rev up metabolism and increase body heat)…

The questions and intense scientific/medical discussion lasted two hours, and I was exhausted.

When we were finished, I went to the walk-in refrigerator and brought out the metal pan with the organs of the deceased patient. Dr. Hollis carefully examined each one with Layne and me. There was nothing dramatic to see, just various lesions typical of shock.

That finished up the review. Layne left to do other tasks. Dr. Hollis gave me some directions about what pathologic lesions to photograph, and what areas to be sure to sample for microscopic examination. "Well thought out," said Dr. Hollis as he left.

CHAPTER 9

The pathology department had two people assigned to teach the lab sections of the pathology course – a resident like me, and a faculty member. The laboratory where we taught was basically a room full of chairs at benches with microscopes on top. The second-year class of two hundred medical students was broken up into smaller groups of about twenty students for each lab. Following a pathology lecture, the students filed into the laboratory to apply what they had learned in the lecture. The students spent their time looking through microscopes at glass slides from teaching sets that demonstrated the topic of the day – infections, lung diseases, cancer…whatever.

The faculty member and I had two jobs:

1. At the beginning of the lab period, one of us gave a brief lecture on the topic of the day by using a special microscope to project the images on a screen. We pointed out what to look for.

2. Then, as the students looked at the slides themselves with their microscopes, we were available to answer any questions the students had.

Sometimes Dr. Hollis walked through the lab as well. One time, a student named Meredith looked at a slide and exclaimed, "Sarcoidosis! That must be really rare. I've never even heard of it."

Dr. Hollis said to the student, loud enough for all to hear, "Mr. Meredith, there are a great many diseases that you have not heard of, which are not necessarily rare."

CHAPTER 10

Of course, there was more to completing an autopsy than presenting it to Dr. Hollis or one of the other faculty members. That was just the start. We took photographs of the pertinent findings, often pointed out by Dr. Hollis. That entailed cleaning up the tissue, including getting rid of any excess blood, and making sure the pathologic findings showed up – sometimes this would require a pointer. There always had to be a ruler in the picture to help demonstrate the size of the lesion, and, of course, a slip with the identifying number of the autopsy. It took some time to stage all that.

Then the paperwork could bury you. The completed autopsy report consisted of the following:

1. Consent form.

2. Clinical history.

3. Gross examination findings. The part of the report that detailed the findings at the time the autopsy was performed – external exam, internal exam, weights and dimensions of each organ, pathologic findings of each organ...

4. Microscopic findings – the results of looking at microscopic slides demonstrating the lesions discovered with the gross examination.

5. Special studies. The results of studies not routinely done – postmortem cultures, cytogenetic studies...

6. Final summary, with correlation of the pathologic findings with the clinical findings.

7. Cause of death.

8. Manner of death.

We dictated this information using a Dictaphone, which was basically a microphone hooked up to a tape recorder. The transcriptionists listened to the tapes and typed the information using an IBM electric typewriter. The typing was always flawless.

To complete an autopsy was a long drawn-out process, with possibilities for screwups all along the way. I remember one time a patient died of pancreatitis, inflammation of the pancreas. When I looked at the microscopic slides, I could not find a single slide of the pancreas, let alone the pancreatitis. I call that a screwup, when I do not have a slide demonstrating what caused the patient's death. I retrieved the formalin bottle containing the tissue samples I had collected at the time of the postmortem exam, and submitted more tissue. Luckily, one of the slides showed the pancreas and pancreatitis. Even then, I still ended up with only *one slide* demonstrating the pancreatitis, the cause of death of the patient.

I still call that a screwup.

Another time I examined a patient who died with a mucopolysaccharide disorder. I duly documented the abnormal mucopolysaccharide deposits in the heart, the liver, and elsewhere – in my report and in the microscopic slides. The cause of death was obvious – these mucopolysaccharides where they were not supposed to be, gumming up the anatomic works. A few months later this patient with this rare genetic disorder was presented at a death conference. Neurologists, neurosurgeons, internists, geneticists, radiologists, and everyone else who took care of this patient with this tragic hereditary disease attended. I was there too. The attention of the conference turned to some poorly understood radiologic changes in the patient's dura mater, brain coverings, especially those near the base of the brain. Were these changes mucopolysaccharide deposits? Was it some congenital malformation related to the patient's hereditary disease? Was it something else – say an infection? The radiologist exhibited the X-rays showing these abnormalities, and *everyone* there commented that they sure wondered what was going on there, at the base of the brain. That question had not been answered during life (as far as I knew, it had not been *asked* during life). So thank goodness, an autopsy had been performed, so this question would be answered, and the pathologist who had done the autopsy, Dr. Spenser, was present. Everyone knew that Dr. Spenser had undoubtedly carefully examined the dura matter at the base of the brain, taken samples for microscopic exam, and therefore would answer the question and show photomicrographs of what everyone in the room saw on the X-rays. Never before or since have I so completely captured the attention of a roomful of people. Everyone turned to me, expectantly, for the answer to the question: WHAT WAS THE PATHOLOGY AT THE BASE OF THE BRAIN?

I had no idea.

There was nothing in my autopsy report about changes in the dura mater at the base of the brain, nor had I sampled any tissue from the dura mater at the base of the brain. I hadn't documented anything there in particular, no abnormalities, no nothing. I hadn't seen anything of note when I did the postmortem exam months earlier. I had no idea what the radiologist was seeing and what everyone was talking about. The first I heard of this abnormality of the dura mater at the base of the brain was at the conference! I had no answers to their question. None.

I call that a screwup.

We had three months to complete a case, more than enough time. If a report was not finished in that time frame, it went on a delinquent list. In my time at Southeastern, I only had two cases on the list, and both times it was because of delays by the same attending faculty member. None of my cases with Dr. Hollis ended up on the delinquent list.

Other residents were not so fortunate. Lloyd Wagner was a third-year resident when I started, and we hit it off. We both grew up in Kansas, and we both liked sports. Lloyd was a talented football player in high school, a running back who played for our biggest rival – Wichita West.

Like me, Lloyd had gone to another medical school before doing his residency at Southeastern, and his first year, like me, he started on the autopsy service. He struggled to keep up. He told me that the more the work piled up, the more stressed he got, so he couldn't concentrate, so his productivity went down, and the work piled up some more. It was a vicious cycle. Lloyd ended up with a large collection of autopsy cases on the delinquent list. It was only a matter of time before there was a reckoning.

Lloyd was in his office, by himself, trying to get organized. Dr. Hollis opened the door, sauntered in with his lanky walk, pulled up a chair, and sat next to Lloyd.

"About these cases of yours," said Dr. Hollis. "They're piling up, dozens of them on the delinquent list. Nobody else has any! What's going on?"

"I don't really have a good explanation. I guess some residents are just slower than others."

"Slow!? Son, you're stopped!"

CHAPTER 11

One of Dr. Hollis's lectures to the second-year medical students was not about pathology per se, but about what it meant to be a physician. "What is the purpose of a physician?" he asked.

A student answered, "To save lives."

"Well, if that is our purpose, then we should turn in our medical licenses and do something else, because we are complete and utter failures. We have not ever saved one single solitary life. Everyone dies."

Another student said the purpose of medicine was to prolong lives. That led to another discussion about quality of life and pain. In Dr. Hollis's view, the purpose of medicine is to alleviate pain; it's that simple.

Which is a surprising answer, coming from a pathologist. Pathologists do very little to alleviate pain. We don't prescribe painkillers. If there is abdominal pain due to acute appendicitis, a surgeon takes out the diseased appendix to get rid of the pain. A pathologist will look at that appendix and make a diagnosis and confirm or not confirm the diagnosis of acute appendicitis, or diagnose something else – maybe a tumor. But it is the surgeon who gets rid of the pain. Similarly, if a patient has painful joints because of gout, an internal medicine specialist will prescribe the appropriate drugs to treat the gout and get rid of the pain. A pathologist may diagnose the gout by looking through a microscope and seeing urate crystals on a glass slide, but it is the internal medicine specialist who gets rid of the pain.

Nevertheless, I think pathologists do relieve pain, although this is done in a rather indirect fashion. I've already given one example that a diagnosis of gout may be made by a pathologist, and treated by an internist – success takes both doctors. Similarly, if a breast mass is benign, the treatment stops and no further operations are required, so no more pain; if the mass is malignant, additional surgery or other treatments may be indicated, to cure the malignancy and avoid the associated pain. Again, a pathologist is an important part of the process.

What pathologists do, study the science of disease and make appropriate accurate diagnoses on specimens, is interesting and important. It is also very hard. If one has a knack for pathology (and relatively few do), one can learn the craft of pathology with a lot of work, study, and effort.

I had no idea whether I could do this.

Speaking to the second-year medical students, Dr. Hollis went on to say that some in the class might go on to be leaders in the community, serve on school boards, and hold office in various organizations. Dr. Hollis said that would be fine, but not to think that some talents and abilities in medicine necessarily made a person qualified for leadership roles in other activities.

In the 1970s, a different time and place than now, that needed to be said.

CHAPTER 12

Following the morning pathology lecture, the students filed into the laboratory to meet with a faculty member and me and then to study on their own. As happened from time to time, Dr. Hollis joined us. He walked in, gently and carefully pushing a small metal table with dark rubber wheels and a cork dissecting board on top. A pan sat next to the board. As Dr. Hollis made his way into the lab, everyone made way, as if it were Moses parting the Red Sea. When he reached a stopping point, the twenty or students arranged themselves in a semicircle, with Dr. Hollis on one side of the table and the students on the other side, a makeshift classroom. The quiet was like that part of the wedding ceremony immediately after the minister asks if anyone objects. No one spoke.

With his latex-gloved hands, Dr. Hollis took a liver and an esophagus out of the pan. Neither organ was normal. What followed was what's called "an organ recital."

A normal liver has a smooth surface and is roughly the size and shape of a fireman's hat but with the color of mahogany, not bright red. The liver Dr. Hollis uncovered was not red or mahogany, but was pale yellow and had a marbled appearance, with the marbles separated by white fibrous tissue (scar). Thus, the normal anatomy was distorted, and the outer surface was not smooth but sunken in some areas and bulging in others.

The esophagus was filled with blood, and abnormally large bulging blood vessels were the obvious source of the bleeding.

Dr. Hollis removed the excessive blood with paper towels and put them in a red biohazard bag. He then raised his right arm and pointed in a straight line to a hapless medical student (some students told me that lightning came out of his fingers, but from where I was standing, I cannot confirm this). The dialogue that followed went something like this:

"What is this organ?" Dr. Hollis asked.

"A liver," stammered the student.

"Excellent. Is this a normal liver?"

"No."

"What's wrong with it?"

"Cirrhosis of the liver."

"Can there be cirrhosis of any other organ?"

After a beat or two, "No."

"Then just say cirrhosis, we haven't got all day. How did you come to that spurious diagnosis?"

"I see the scarring extending to the surface, the regenerating nodules…"

"To the surface, do you mean to the capsule?"

"I'm not sure the liver has a capsule."

"You mean to say the liver doesn't have a capsule?"

"Uh, I guess."

"That would be very interesting information to Dr. Frances Glisson, who described the capsule of the liver named after him in 1654. What kind of students are they sending me these days, who don't even know their anatomy? Let's move on to the esophagus. What do you see?"

"Changes of a massive bleed."

"Bleed is a verb."

"Changes of massive hemorrhage."

"Did the cirrhosis cause the hemorrhage in the esophagus?"

"I think so."

"You think so. How?"

"Like it says in the textbook…" The student did a good job explaining the pathologic mechanisms (pathophysiology) that led to the untoward series of events in the patient.

"What was the cause of the cirrhosis in this patient?"

The student was stumped. After a few seconds, but it seemed longer, the student said, "I don't know."

Dr. Hollis stood motionless briefly and then said, "Son, you can't not know. You are a doctor and patients will come to you and depend on you for answers, and you will have to help them, and to help them, you will have to know what is wrong with them. How can you treat cirrhosis if you don't know what causes cirrhosis?"

The student replied that he was just a student and not a doctor yet.

Dr. Hollis did not reply to what he clearly regarded as an asinine comment, and went on to question me. Everyone was fair game.

I answered, "Two possible causes are viral hepatitis and chronic alcoholism."

"What was the cause of the cirrhosis in this liver?"

I looked. I had no idea. "I don't know," I said.

"You can't not know." Dr. Hollis then explained the pathologic changes, which in this case were characteristic of chronic alcohol abuse, and how these changes were different than what would be seen in cirrhosis caused by viral hepatitis.

Clearly disappointed in me, he asked, "How can you sleep at night, knowing so little?"

I hadn't slept hardly at all since I started my internship.

I will tell you this, though, at the end of that laboratory session, everyone in the room knew the name Glisson's capsule as well as their own name, and from then on I knew the differences between cirrhosis caused by viral hepatitis and chronic alcoholism, information I have used thousands of times since then to make diagnoses on liver biopsies from real live patients.

CHAPTER 13

I was in Dr. Hollis's office, going over some slides from an autopsy.

His office had two rooms. One was basically a projection room, with a projector at one end and a screen at the other. Dr. Hollis used this room for many purposes – to prepare lectures, prepare for conferences such as clinicopathologic conferences (CPCs), and to teach histology to interns, like me.

The other room, where we were, had a lot more stuff. Behind Dr. Hollis's chair and desk, there was a small refrigerator in the corner, where Dr. Hollis kept his Coca-Colas. Each side of the wall separating the two rooms was bare. On the opposite side, however, was a bench covered with file cabinets containing index cards. Each index card had a description and summary of medical information Dr. Hollis had gleaned from medical journals, handouts, and books. The information was filed by subject – tuberculosis, lung cancer, coronary artery disease, and every disease known to man.

The remaining two walls had floor-to-ceiling bookshelves packed with books. Many of the books were old, the type you find at an antique bookstore. Dr. Hollis revered the old masters of pathology and medicine; he thought that they were geniuses. "We aren't any smarter than they were, probably not as smart," he said many times.

Rudolph Virchow's classic textbook *Cellular Pathology* sat on the shelf, an original edition, published in 1858. Dr. Virchow was Prussian and a contemporary of Otto von Bismarck.

Dr. Ludwig Aschoff's *Lectures in Pathology* was also in the collection, again an original edition, published in 1924. Dr. Aschoff was a German physician and pathologist who has many pathologic entities named after him.

The author's pages of these old books contained photographs of these giants of medicine – stern unsmiling visages that mirrored the most common expression of Dr. Hollis. It was a Scrooge "Bah, humbug" look. Not surprisingly, we knew it was the Christmas season when Dr. Hollis hung a picture of Scrooge on the door to his office, with the caption "Bah, humbug" – a charming tradition.

We were sitting across from each other at a teaching microscope. The base (bottom) of the microscope was flanked by two focusing knobs; a halogen lamp light source was front and center. The lamp sent light up to a stage, a ledge if you will, with an aperture to let the light in. The microscope slide to be examined was placed on this stage. The light shined through the tissue on the slide to an objective, a fancy magnifying glass. There were four objectives that could be rotated into position to look at the tissue: 4X, which magnified tissue 4 times; 10X, which magnified tissue 10 times; 40X, which magnified tissue 40 times; and 100X, which magnified tissue 100 times. The light then went up a tube (called a head) to the two eyepieces, which is what we looked through to see the magnified images. Each eyepiece had a lens with an additional magnification of 10X.

We used a teaching microscope with two heads, each with eyepieces, so Dr. Hollis and I could each see the same thing as we looked through the microscope. Dr. Hollis pushed the slides one by one across the stage with his left hand while using his right hand to turn one of the two focusing knobs near the bottom of the microscope to bring the magnified images into view.

The refrigerator hummed faintly in the background. Dr. Hollis slid his chair over to the refrigerator and grabbed a six-ounce bottle of Coca-Cola for himself. He asked me if I wanted one. Well, yeah. Dr. Hollis handed me a six-ounce bottle of Coca-Cola. Little beads of condensed water moistened my right hand.

We were interrupted by Dr. John Leonard, an internist, and his entourage of third- and fourth-year medical students as well as his residents and interns. Dr. Leonard was one of the more famous physicians on the faculty. He was handsome and charismatic and was periodically on national public television when they wanted his insight on some medical issue. In my opinion he was an excellent doctor.

Dr. Leonard had some microscopic slides that he wanted Dr. Hollis to take a look at. Dr. Leonard was taking care of a female patient and did not know what was causing the lady's illness. Dr. Leonard hoped that Dr. Hollis could come up with a diagnosis, in a fashion similar to that maverick Dr. Gregory House on the TV drama *House.*

I hate that show. I know so many people who love it and tell me how smart Dr. House is, how he takes the toughest cases, the patients who are the most challenging to diagnose and treat, and how Dr. House always rises to the challenge, making the diagnosis and curing the patient. I know it's escape fiction, but come on. If I had hours and days to work on the diagnosis of ONE PATIENT and had access to every test and procedure available to mankind, without regard to cost or scheduling, well, I would look pretty smart too.

And my dear readers say, "Dr. Spenser, jealousy does not become you."

Dr. Leonard presented Dr. Hollis with microscopic slides of lung from the patient. This 23 twenty-three-year-old patient came to the emergency room after fainting. The cause turned out to be low blood oxygen due to lung disease. The radiologic studies showed some abnormal lung changes but were nonspecific. The patient had a bronchoscopy, which collected lung tissue for examination by our surgical pathology department. Unfortunately the results of the surgical pathology exam were as nonspecific as the X-ray findings. Dr. Leonard was at a dead end, with no diagnosis for this unfortunate woman. Dr. Leonard wanted Dr. Hollis's help on the case, including examining the slides from the bronchoscopy specimen. This was not unusual. Often when Dr. Leonard had a diagnostic challenge, and there was a tissue specimen available, he asked Dr. Hollis to review the case.

Dr. Hollis listened to Dr. Leonard relate this patient's information as he looked through the microscope. When Dr. Leonard finished, Dr. Hollis asked the medical students, "What is the purpose of clinical microscopy?"

After some discussion, the consensus answer to this "what am I thinking type of question" was that by examining the slides carefully, one could come up with a diagnosis that could be used to help the patient, get rid of pain, and help her quality of life.

That out of the way, Dr. Hollis continued to look at the slides, which were quite beautiful, an array of various shades of blue from the hematoxylin stain, and red from the eosin stain, with combinations resulting in every hue and shade imaginable. The exact chemical reactions that lead to this symphony of colors on a slide are unknown; like much of medicine, it's witchcraft. There were unstained zones on the slide as well, especially the air spaces in the lung, which were clear.

Dr. Hollis examined the slides of the lung one by one. His right hand was on the focusing knob, turning it to bring the slide into focus as he gently moved the slide across the stage with his left hand.

It was a tough case. I knew that because Dr. Hollis would periodically take his right hand and rub the hair at the top of his head, his "tell" that it was a tough case.

Dr. Hollis solved the case, though. He adjusted the microscope to look at the slide with polarized light, which revealed crystal deposits, which lit up like a nighttime New York City skyline viewed from the top of the Empire State Building. They were talc crystals, within the blood vessels, not air spaces, which meant they went to the lung via the bloodstream, not breathing.

"Does this patient use drugs?" asked Dr. Hollis.

Dr. Leonard answered that the patient had denied using drugs. They had not collected blood or urine for a drug screen.

"Better ask again, and order a drug screen," said Dr. Hollis. As everyone took turns looking at the slide, he pointed out that talc is used in oral medications as a bulking and lubricating agent. If an oral drug like oxycodone is, in fact, taken orally like it is supposed to, the talc does not cause problems because the gastrointestinal system can take care of it. However, if oxycodone is injected into the bloodstream instead, the results can be catastrophic, because the talc ends up deposited in the lung, where it causes problems. The talc doesn't dissolve but floats like driftwood in the bloodstream. Just as driftwood travels along until something stops it, so does the talc travel along until it reaches the small capillaries of the lungs, where it piles up so the lungs become a beach buried in driftwood and other trash, with comparable problems.

Upon further questioning and investigation by Dr. Leonard, the patient confessed to injecting illicit narcotics, even covertly while in the hospital. Thus the appropriate medical and psychiatric treatments were initiated for the patient – no guarantee of cure, of course, but at least she would have a chance.

House couldn't have done any better.

CHAPTER 14

About his pathology course and his tests, Dr. Hollis repeatedly told the second-year students that "I will not flunk you with trick questions; I will flunk you by attrition."

There were periodic unannounced practical exams, pop quizzes, given during our laboratory time. The students had to look at ten microscopic slides, make diagnoses, and answer questions about what was demonstrated. Dr. Hollis graded the papers as they were handed in. The tests were tough, and knowing the answers to all the questions was about impossible.

But it did happen. Somehow one of our better students answered all ten questions correctly – a score of 100%. Needless to say, the student was quite proud of his performance, with a beaming countenance and a bounce to his walk.

"How did you cheat?" growled Dr. Hollis.

The student was crushed.

CHAPTER 15

Dr. Hollis had interests other than pathology. He was well-read. Of course he had read Sir Arthur Conan Doyle's Sherlock Holmes stories. Dr. Hollis patterned his life after Sherlock Holmes. He had the same kind of index card files that Holmes used. Dr. Hollis liked to use deductive reasoning to make his diagnoses, the same reasoning Holmes used to solve his cases. Dr. Hollis would often quote Holmes; for example, whenever he made an unusual or controversial diagnosis of a rare disease or condition, he would say, "Once you have eliminated the impossible, whatever remains, however improbable, must be the truth" – the correct diagnosis.

Dr. Hollis not only read all the Sherlock Holmes stories, he read all the works by Sir Arthur Conan Doyle, including *The Lost World,* which he loaned to me, an original edition from 1912. It was probably pretty valuable, and I'm glad I didn't lose it.

Dr. Hollis liked the poem *The Wonderful One-Hoss Shay* by Oliver Wendell Holmes. Dr. Hollis applied it to autopsy pathology. The poem, written in 1858 (Dr. Hollis's favorite time period) describes a carriage built to such a high standard that it would not break down. The poem notes that a carriage usually breaks down because of some weakness – in the harness, the wheels, floorboards, a bolt…something; so it is not the carriage itself that breaks down, but it is always some weakness in some part of the carriage that leads to problems. For example, the harness would break, but everything else in the carriage would work fine. Or the wheels might wear out, but everything else works fine, and so forth.

The theory explored in the poem was that if one built a carriage with no weaknesses, it would not break down and would last forever.

The trick of construction, then, was to use the finest leather for the harness so it would not break down, and the finest rubber for the wheels so they would not wear out, the best wood for the floorboard, the highest quality steel for the bolts and so on. Such a venerable vehicle would last forever.

Of course this theory could apply to the human body. Many patients die of heart attacks, so if a patient exercises and had a good diet, his heart will not give out. If a patient drinks plenty of water, the kidneys will keep working and the patient will not die of renal failure. If a person does not smoke, the patient's lungs will keep working. Thus, a patient who takes care of each of his organ systems, like the One Hoss Shay, will never break down and will never die.

Alas, that is not the way the poem ends. The carriage does not last forever, but eventually breaks down:

"It went to pieces all at once, –

All at once, and nothing first –

Just as bubbles do when they burst."

A human body can be like that, everything breaking down seemingly all at once. Several times Dr. Hollis and I used that metaphor for patients who sometimes lived into their nineties, in good health right to the last, when everything broke down – heart, kidneys, brain…seemingly all at once.

An eighty-one-year-old woman was profoundly demented due to Alzheimer's disease. She was admitted to the hospital with what her doctors regarded as "nonspecific pneumonia" and died a few days later

At autopsy, she did indeed have a fairly advanced bronchopneumonia, which might have caused her death, but she also had several other serious disease processes that could have caused her death:

1. Multiple ischemic infarcts in the brain (strokes) secondary to arteriosclerotic vascular disease.

2. Severe coronary artery heart disease.

3. End stage renal failure secondary to hypertensive kidney disease.

4. Severe urinary tract infection.

5. Finally, the previously mentioned bronchopneumonia, with sepsis, secondary to aspiration of food contents.

All these conditions were in addition to the Alzheimer's disease, which was demonstrated in the sections of the brain. We used a silver stain on the microscopic slides to demonstrate the tangles, which looked like starfish, and the plaques, which looked like tumbleweeds – really quite picturesque – beautiful lesions of a horrible disease.

There were several candidates for the cause of death, and my choice was the bronchopneumonia with sepsis. I was quite surprised when Dr. Hollis insisted that the cause of death was Alzheimer's disease.

Huh?

"This lady died because she was unable to tell her doctors what was wrong with her."

Chapter 16

Dr. Hollis loved language. A macrophage is a cell in the body that does cleanup duty. But to Dr. Holli this cell was not a macrophage but a "lurking macrophage."

Dr. Hollis was enamored by the word "frank." An infected wound was not filled with pus, but "frank pus." A lower extremity would not be amputated because of gangrene but "frank gangrene." A lung was not edematous, but instead had "frank pulmonary edema" and so forth.

To be frank, he went overboard with the word "frank," and some of the med students teased him about it.

Cut to a pathology lecture late in the course, when the students were half asleep, and everyone was about ready to get the semester over with. One of the students had a propensity to sleep during the lectures, so Dr. Hollis had given him a pillow and some eye shades so he could rest more comfortably.

The lights were turned off, and Dr. Hollis proceeded to project Kodachrome after Kodachrome on the white screen, rapid fire, cramming the students full of pathology knowledge.

Suddenly a door in the back slammed open, and a big belligerent fellow with a fierce expression bolted into the lecture hall. He turned on the lights. Everyone was startled, including Dr. Hollis. Dr. Hollis regained his composure and explained to the man that class was in session, and that he was not welcome.

Unfazed by Dr. Hollis, the man did not stop but advanced toward Dr. Hollis in a threatening fashion, telling Dr. Hollis that he was there to "settle the score, because you have been saying bad things about me..."

The menacing man drew closer to Dr. Hollis, and the conflict seemed about to escalate. Dr. Hollis certainly wasn't going to back down, and neither, it seemed, was this madman. Some of the students got out of their seats to protect Dr. Hollis from this lunatic when Dr. Hollis asked, "Who are you?"

"Frank!" the man answered, turned around, and walked away.

It was quiet for one beat, and then the class exploded in laughter.

For your amusement, this was a one-act play written by Dr. Hollis, produced by Dr. Hollis, and starring Dr. Hollis.

CHAPTER 17

Mostly Dr. Hollis taught us residents the nuts and bolts of pathology. On days there was not an autopsy to review, Dr. Hollis taught histology to the first-year residents (interns). These classes met at 6 a.m. in Dr. Hollis's office, the side of the office with a projector and a screen. Dr. Hollis used a teaching set with Kodachrome slides to demonstrate the histology of all the organ systems.

The four interns (Sid Steinberg, Fred Adams, Layne Siler and I) made up the class along with Mary Hemphill, a second-year resident who also attended the sessions. Mary was a Cajun who had gone to medical school at Louisiana State University and had also done one year of pathology there before transferring to Southeastern.

Dr. Hollis wrote the histology textbook we used, creatively called *Textbook of Human Histology* by Hollis, Darrell. The three interns from Southeastern – Sid, Fred, and Layne – had already read the book, of course, and used Dr. Hollis's textbook for their histology course during medical school. Mary and I had not used Dr. Hollis's textbook for our histology courses.

If there was no autopsy to review, our assignment was to read the chapter on the topic to be discussed, and show up at 6 a.m. the next morning ready to answer questions. At the teaching sessions, Dr. Hollis projected Kodachrome slides demonstrating the material, and as he did so, he quizzed us in his usual Socratic style. It was a good idea to be prepared. It could get pretty bloody if any of us showed up unprepared.

One day the topic for discussion was normal bone marrow histology, one of the most complicated systems to review. A normal bone marrow has a bewildering number of cells of different types, more or less haphazardly arranged. There are three main cell lines, but then it gets complicated very quickly.

As usual, Dr. Hollis projected photomicrographs demonstrating the features of the bone marrow, and asked question after question about each slide. The room was shadowy; the only light source was the slide projector sending images onto the white screen. It was a bloody session, the blood coming not from the bone marrow, but out of the hides of the residents.

Dr. Hollis pointed to one cell that didn't fit any of the three cell lines. It was an unusual-looking cell. The nucleus was not in the center of the cell where it usually is, but eccentric, to one side. The cytoplasm was stained a deep blue with sparkles like stars in the night sky, but the sky was not black but a deep blue like sunset at the beach. The overall effect was quite beautiful actually.

Unfortunately when Dr. Hollis asked me what the cell was, I didn't know. "Lord only knows," I said.

Dr. Hollis asked Sid Steinberg to name the cell, and he said, "A sea blue histiocyte" – an apt name I have not forgotten.

"Thank you, Lord," said Dr. Hollis.

Dr. Hollis's histology course was complete and meticulous. Dr. Hollis wanted us to look good when we became practicing pathologists. So when it came time to study the endometrium, he wanted us to know the histologic pattern of every single day of the endometrial cycle, from day one to day twenty-eight. For him it was not good enough to discern whether an endometrium was in menstrual phase, proliferative phase, or secretory phase – any pathologist could do that. Dr. Hollis wanted us to recognize the exact day of the cycle. He thought it would make us look good in the eyes of our ob-gyn colleagues. Dr. Hollis wanted the gynecologists to exclaim: "Those Southeastern-trained pathologists don't just tell me the phase of the endometrium I send them; they tell me the exact day!"

So the day we covered the histology of the normal endometrium, Dr. Hollis quizzed us as the Kodachrome slides went round and round on the carousel, taking their turns to be projected on the screen – *click…click…click.* Dr. Hollis demonstrated the characteristic microscopic changes that occurred each day of the endometrial cycle days: proliferative phase day 1, 2, 3, 4...14, ovulation, secretory phase day 16, 17, 18...and ending with the changes in the endometrium during menstruation.

After each slide, Dr. Hollis asked Mary Hemphill, "Is this a safe time for sex?"

Each time Mary answered, "There is no safe time for sex."

When we finished the lesson, Dr. Hollis said, "Next session we will cover the vagina, which will be easier than the endometrium, because there are no glands in the vagina* except the glans penis from time to time."

Mary said, "You are a male chauvinist."

"That's the nicest thing anyone has ever said to me."

*(Author's note: There are glands in the vagina.)

Chapter 18

Another war story from the lecture hall:

Dr. Hollis began projecting slides from an autopsy on to the white screen at the front. The images demonstrated that the patient had died of a stroke, because a large thromboembolus (clot) had obstructed one of the carotid arteries, with resultant loss of blood flow to the brain, and a resultant fatal infarct (stroke). The following exchange took place with one of the students, which started out well, but ended not so well:

Dr. Hollis: Please, if you will, identify the lesion that caused this fatal brain infarct.

Student: A thromboembolus, occluding a large carotid artery.

Dr. Hollis: Excellent. Do you think this thromboembolus caused the massive infarct in the brain?

Student: Yes.

Dr. Hollis: Did this thromboembolus originate in the carotid artery because of the arteriosclerosis of the artery, or did it come from elsewhere?

Student: Elsewhere.

Dr. Hollis: Why?

Student: Because it is not attached to the wall of the artery.

Dr. Hollis: Excellent. Since the thromboembolus did not arise in the carotid artery, where did it come from?

Student: It probably came from veins in the lower extremities and migrated to the carotid artery.

Dr. Hollis: So you believe there was a condition in the legs of this patient leading to the formation of this thromboembolus. Perhaps she had been relatively inactive, because of her obesity or some other health issue, and her blood didn't circulate very well, which predisposed her to this problem?

The student nodded yes.

Dr. Hollis: The thromboembolus then left the legs and traveled up the inferior vena cava, to the right side of the heart?

The student nodded yes, happy that Dr. Hollis was agreeing with him. Explanations always sounded so reasonable and smart when delivered by Dr. Hollis.

Dr. Hollis: At this point this large thromboembolus went to the lungs, where it met the pulmonary capillaries, and at this point, the large thromboembolus inexplicably shrank to microscopic size so it could traverse those capillaries, after which it reached larger vessels and miraculously reformed into its original large size and eventually obstructed this carotid artery. An amazing feat for a thromboembolus, to my knowledge never before reported or described in the medical literature. It reminds me of *Fantastic Voyage* in which a submarine crew is shrunk to microscopic size and placed into the circulation of the body of an injured scientist so they can repair damage to his brain, and after doing so they revert to normal size. But that was *science fiction*.

Student: I still think it came from the leg.

Dr. Hollis: How did it get from the leg to the carotid artery?

Student: Good question.

Dr. Hollis: All my questions are good. It is the answers that are so bad.

Student: I don't know.

Dr. Hollis: You can't not know.

It turned out that the patient had an atrial septal defect of the heart, which meant this: There is a tissue wall that separates the right atrium from the left atrium, called the septum. Of course, usually this structure is intact, keeping blood from free-flowing from the right side of the heart to the left side of the heart, outside of the normal circulation. But in this patient there was a hole where the septum was open (patent). Thus blood could abnormally flow from the right side of the heart to the left side of the heart, and the thromboembolus (clot) could take a shortcut from the right side of the heart to the left side of the heart, bypassing the lung with its small capillaries, and directly reach the large carotid arteries, with fatal consequences.

Dr. Hollis: You did well on the origin of this thromboembolus; you just need a little more knowledge about possible pathways.

CHAPTER 19

My six-month rotation on Dr. Hollis's autopsy rotation continued.

Layne Siler, my fellow intern, presented a case to Dr. Hollis. The patient had died after a fairly routine operation, a ventral hernia repair. I regard this as major surgery, even though fairly routine. As a surgeon friend of mine once said, though, "There is no operation so simple or so routine that you can't fuck it up."

I don't know if the operation was fucked up or not, but the patient died about ten days after the operation. He just kind of dwindled away. The reasons for his demise were obscure. The autopsy was done in hopes of finding out what had gone wrong, so that similar problems could be avoided in the future.

Layne was mystified as to what had gone wrong, which was a bad predicament to be in when presenting a case to Dr. Hollis. Layne had carefully examined the heart, opening the coronary arteries and then opening the heart along the lines of the blood flow, as we had been taught. He hadn't found anything too dramatic. There was some arteriosclerosis in the coronary arteries, but nothing to unequivocally prove that coronary artery disease, or anything related to the heart, had caused the death of the patient.

Unfortunately for Layne, it didn't take long for Dr. Hollis to find the heart disease that had killed the patient. He made an incision into the left ventricle to expose an obvious myocardial infarct. It was large, about four inches by one inch, not huge, but large enough to cause death by heart attack.

What I love about pathology is that it makes sense. There were well-defined pathological changes that indicated the heart attack had happened about ten days prior to death, exactly matching the history of a ten-day postoperative downhill clinical course.

And if you could strip away the fact that this lesion had caused the death of a patient, the whole appearance was beautiful – an island of distinct colorful yellowish gray (but dead) myocardium surrounded by reefs of bright yellow reacting white blood cells and pinkish red blood vessels lying in a sea of red myocardium.

The experience was not beautiful for Layne. It was awful, because he had totally missed the myocardial infarct, the cause of death of the patient, which was one of the big reasons to do the autopsy in the first place. As the myocardial infarct was demonstrated, the exchange between Dr. Hollis and Layne went something like this:

Layne: I just missed it.

Dr. Hollis: You sure did. In twenty years of teaching residents, I have never seen a more inept, poorly prepared case. I don't see how in the world you could miss this obvious myocardial infarct. I'm extremely disappointed.

It went downhill from there.

Later that day, John Henderson, one of the fourth-year residents, came to our office. He asked Layne, "How do you feel?"

"Shitty," he answered.

I was determined such a fate would not happen to me. The next autopsy I performed was similar in that I felt I had to rule out a cardiac cause of death. So I was quite thorough when it came to the dissection of the heart.

First, I dissected the heart in the usual way. Using forceps and a small scissors, I opened all the coronary arteries to make sure they were not narrowed by some arteriosclerosis or thrombus that caused a heart attack resulting in the death of this patient. I found nothing of significance.

Using a strong scissors, then I opened the heart itself, as the blood flowed – the inferior vena cava and superior vena cava, then the right atrium, the tricuspid valve, right ventricle, pulmonary arteries, left atrium, mitral valve, left ventricle, and I finished with the origin of the aorta. Everything was normal.

This was routine, and it was what Layne had done, and doing so, he had missed an obvious myocardial infarct, the cause of death, a big mistake, and one that was not going to happen to me.

So...using a large knife, I serially sectioned the ventricles, with particular attention to the left ventricle, looking at each slice of cardiac muscle for any evidence of a myocardial infarct, something that might have caused the demise of this patient. Whatever was there, I was not going to miss it. I looked everywhere carefully. The exam had to be meticulous; the outer surface of the heart was relatively smooth, like a flat tin roof, with only the coronary arteries coursing along the surface. But the inner surfaces were not smooth at all, more like a corrugated ceiling, with ridges and grooves formed by the active cardiac muscles. I examined every millimeter.

I didn't find an infarct or any significant pathology. Nevertheless, I was proud of my handiwork. I put the slices of the heart back together as best I could and wrapped everything together in a moist paper towel. I was eager to show Dr. Hollis how complete and thorough my investigation of the heart had been.

The next morning Dr. Hollis gently removed the moist paper towel to reveal the heart. As he did so, the various parts of the heart, which had been nicely held together by the paper towel, well, they kind of slid over the cutting board, like a slinky toy going down stair steps.

Dr. Hollis shook his head with a disgusted look on his face and said, "What did you do to this heart, throw it up in the air and start hacking at it?"

CHAPTER 20

Dr. Hollis stood in front of the second-year pathology class and announced that the lecture would cover the diseases associated with excess weight – diabetes, coronary artery disease, hypertension…it was a long list. Dr. Hollis leaned forward and looked at a "chunky" student and stated, "Obesity is a *loathsome* disease."

One of the students in my lab had a habit of asking brownie-point-type questions, the kind of questions that did not really indicate a lack of understanding of the material, but the direct opposite, like "Could you please help me understand the article in the most recent *New England Journal of Medicine*, which postulates that cellular immunity may have a surveillance function in preventing neoplasia, whereas the editorial in that same issue takes a more cautious approach as to whether or not this finding can be used to treat cancer and that there are challenges to doing so. What do you think?"

Of course, the correct answer was "I think you're a pompous twit."

Dr. Hollis was more diplomatic. He quickly figured out what was going on. After another long-winded question, he replied, "Is that the most burning question you have today?"

This did not deter the clueless student.

At the next organ recital, that student, along with about twenty others, was looking at a kidney, which was large because of a hereditary condition that caused innumerable cysts. It was nonfunctional and causing problems like high blood pressure, so it had been surgically removed. The kidney was on the table.

The students and I were on one side of the table, and Dr. Hollis on the other side. Instead of answering the intelligent but obnoxious student's questions, Dr. Hollis decided to turn the tables and ask the questions. The result was something like this:

Dr. Hollis: What do you see?

Student: This appears to be a kidney.

Dr. Hollis: Is it a kidney or not?

Student: Yes, it's a kidney.

Dr. Hollis: Then say it's a kidney. A kidney can't "appear" and then "disappear"; a kidney "is." Go on.

Student: The kidney is large in size.

Dr. Hollis: I have to interrupt you again. The kidney is indeed large, but you don't need to say large in size, that is redundant.

The student then went into a long soliloquy about how a kidney could be large in size, or large in function, large in capacity…

During this long explanation from the student, who was on his left, Dr. Hollis was gently moving his right arm back and forth, where the student couldn't see it, but the rest of us could, with gestures of "please deliver me from this boredom."

Dr. Hollis was a tough grader. No one in his pathology class that year got an A even though I thought there were some pretty bright students in my lab group.

Flash forward. At the end of the second year of medical school, all the second-year students in all the medical schools across the land take the part one test on the Basic Sciences administered by the National Board of Medical Examiners. As the name implies, the test covers the basic sciences portions of the first two years of medical school – biochemistry, pharmacology, anatomy, and so forth.

Part two is taken at the end of the fourth year of medical school and covers the clinical disciplines – internal medicine, surgery, pediatrics, and so forth.

Part three is taken after the internship year and covers clinical topics.

Most states regard the National Board tests as a valid measure of competency, and thus passing these "boards" can be used to qualify for a medical license in most states. The tests are a big deal.

Pathology is covered in Part one of the boards. Every medical student I talked to that year (the class in which no one got an A in pathology) thought that the pathology parts of the board exam were relatively easy. Considering the standards Dr. Hollis set, I wasn't surprised.

The National Board test scores came back. With pride, Dr. Hollis announced to the class that they had finished number one in the country in pathology.

One of the students raised his hand and asked, "Who finished number two?"

"I don't know," answered Dr. Hollis.

The student persisted: "Do you think it might have been Harvard?"

"Hell no!" said Dr. Hollis. "Those Harvard professors don't know any more about real teaching than they do about fornicating!"

"Okay."

Irritated, Dr. Hollis said, "Look, if it's really bothering you, I can probably find out."

"No, that's not necessary, but I wonder if anyone *there* got an A."

CHAPTER 21

Dr. Hollis's commandment to everyone – students, interns, residents – was "you can't not know."

How was that possible? How could anyone have that much experience, to be in a position to always "know" and never "not know"? Every physician, especially a pathologist, from time to time encounters a condition or disease or lesion that the physician has never encountered before, so how could a pathologist/physician never "not know" or, to put it another way, know everything?

Dr. Hollis's answer: To read.

Dr. Hollis preached that a pathologist/physician had to read what was in the textbooks, medical journals, published lectures…One had to *know* the medical literature. That way, when a pathologist/physician encountered a patient or a specimen with a certain disease for the first time, the physician/pathologist would be ready to make a diagnosis, render a treatment, and do what needed to be done – because the physician/pathologist had already read about whatever medical challenge presented itself.

Which was what Dr. Hollis did. He read a lot. He came to work early when no one else was around so that he could read his journals and his books in his office or in the library (he had a key) in peace and quiet, uninterrupted. He used index cards to keep track of what he read. On the index card he wrote the source of the information – journal name, date, page, etc. – and then wrote a succinct concise summary including all the pertinent information in the article. Then he filed the index card in the appropriate category and consulted the index cards when he needed to read up on the topic.

In this respect, as in many others, his model for this approach was Sir Arthur Conan Doyle's character Sherlock Holmes. Dr. Hollis had read all the Sherlock Holmes stories. One of Sherlock Holmes's aids in solving cases was his voluminous files of newspaper clippings and other literature. I remember stories that started out with Holmes working on his files, only to be interrupted by a new client. Sherlock Holmes then sometimes started out the investigation by reviewing pertinent information in his files. I am sure Dr. Hollis imagined himself as Sherlock Holmes. I certainly was Watson.

Dr. Hollis's files of index cards occupied about 25% of his office; they were piled on waist-high benches lined up against a wall.

To do all this, Dr. Hollis had to get an early start, so he came to work very early, earlier than anyone else, about 5 a.m. Set in his ways and disciplined, Dr. Hollis liked to park his car in the same spot every morning. Arriving so early, this was always possible.

Until one of the medical students noticed where Dr. Hollis parked, and arrived about fifteen minutes before Dr. Hollis showed up, and parked in Dr. Hollis's favorite space. The next day Dr. Hollis arrived about fifteen minutes before the student and got his spot back. The following day the student arrived fifteen minutes earlier yet, and beat Dr. Hollis to the parking space. Then Dr. Hollis arrived earlier yet to reclaim his parking spot. This went on for a few more days until Dr. Hollis started arriving at 2 a.m., and the student gave up.

CHAPTER 22

I did an autopsy on a patient who died of acute leukemia. The patient had notable nodular skin lesions, not well characterized during life, so I had sampled them at the time of the autopsy for further study. Dr. Hollis and I were reviewing the microscopic slides of the case. When we came to the skin lesions, Dr. Hollis looked at the slides for a while, then slid his chair back away from the microscope and rubbed the top of his head with his right hand.

Dr. Hal Reed, a pathologist specializing in diseases of the skin (dermatopathologist), had recently joined our faculty. I had been attending his weekly dermatopathology teaching conferences, and I was favorably impressed. He knew his stuff.

Dr. Hollis decided that the two of us would take these slides of the skin lesions to Dr. Reed, ask him to look at them, and hopefully help us. His office was a short walk away.

Dr. Reed was a kindly middle-aged man, hair combed straight back, with the appearance of an organization man out of the 1950s. Being a dermatopathologist is a great life. The specimens are usually small pieces of skin, biopsies, which show up in neat little bottles of formalin, which are processed overnight into slides to look at the next day, no muss, no fuss. The dermatopathologist looks at the slides and renders a diagnosis. Dermatopathology is a nice clean profession with no bloody specimens, no feces to deal with, and no cadavers.

I think Dr. Hollis had a pretty good idea what these skin lesions were, deposits of the leukemia cells, but I think he wanted to check out the new dermatopathologist – see what he knew.

Dr. Reed looked at the slides of the skin in the usual manner – sliding the slide along the microscope stage with his left hand and focusing the microscope using the knob in his right hand. After looking at all the slides, which took five minutes, he put the slides aside and said, "This is a toughie. Let me think about it for a while, and I'll get back to you in the morning."

Dr. Hollis said, "No, you don't need to think about it because the slide won't look any different tomorrow, and you won't be any smarter tomorrow, so you might as well give me your diagnosis now."

Which Dr. Reed did.

CHAPTER 23

The interminable first six months of my internship year continued. Most days there was an autopsy review with Dr. Hollis, which took up most of the morning. In the afternoon there were photographs to take, more autopsies to do, or continue working on the ones we already had – trim tissues for microscopic slides, look at the microscopic slides, go over the findings with Dr. Hollis or the attending assigned to the case, dictate all this stuff, proofread the dictations…the to-do list was endless.

Of course, if there were no autopsies, there was no autopsy review with Dr. Hollis the next morning. Those mornings we interns and Mary Hemphill met in Dr. Hollis's office to go over the assigned histology topic, so I had to prepare for that.

The histology course went on through the summer, into autumn, and finished in late November. By then we had covered all the histology chapters in Dr. Hollis's book. It was time for a test on what we learned. It was one hundred questions. The person with the highest score would be treated to lunch by Dr. Hollis at the Piedmont Club, the best restaurant in the city.

The questions consisted of Dr. Hollis projecting a slide on the screen, then asking a question about it. For example, he pointed to a cell, and the question was "What is this cell?" He showed slides of endometria at various stages of the endometrial cycle, asking us which day of the cycle was demonstrated. We wrote down our answers.

I didn't have to worry about working a lunch with Dr. Hollis into my schedule. I got the lowest score, a seventy. I related the score to Dr. Hollis, who said, "Yuck." Fred Adams got a seventy-one. Mary and Layne had significantly higher scores. My best friend among my fellow interns, Sol Steinberg, won the lunch, with a score in the nineties.

Well, good for him, but not so good for me. I was ashamed of my score.

John Henderson, a fourth-year resident, came to my office that afternoon. It was just the two of us. John was a good ole boy, liked to hunt and fish. His dream when he went in to private practice was to be able to make enough money to afford a ranch and retire early.

"How are you feeling?" he asked.

"Tired of being stupid and making mistakes," I said.

He smiled.

"Is Dr. Hollis still coming down hard on you?" asked John.

"Yes. He's called me the pinnacle of ineptitude."

"That's pretty good. I haven't heard that one. Has he said, 'Even though your mother may love you, you are not a good doctor'?"

"Yeah."

"How about, 'How can you sleep at night knowing so little?' Has he used that one yet?"

"Yeah. On me I'm sure he has used them all."

"Good," said John. "It means he hasn't given up on you. If he gives up on you, he will ignore you because he doesn't want to waste his time on someone who will not be a good pathologist. He challenges you and comes down hard on you because he is trying to make you better. If he stops criticizing you and stops insulting you, that means he has given up on you and it's time to worry."

"Who has he given up on?"

John named a second-year resident and a third-year resident. John was prophetic. The third-year resident's contract was not renewed; she had to finish her pathology training at another medical center. The second-year resident stayed in the program at Southeastern, but switched to doing clinical pathology only – blood banking, chemistry, microbiology, and hematology – but no anatomic pathology, so he would never have to interact with Dr. Hollis again. He had gone to Ivory Medical School, same as me, so he had befriended me when I showed up at Southeastern. When I asked him why he switched to clinical pathology only, he said this: "I just couldn't take it. I didn't have what it takes to survive Dr. Hollis and to learn from him. I wasn't smart enough or talented enough to synthesize information the way Dr. Hollis could."

Of course, my answer to that was that no one could synthesize or think the way Dr. Hollis could.

Anyway, the conversation with John helped me. Dr. Hollis never let up on me at all. He continued to challenge me, and not in a nice way.

CHAPTER 24

Dr. Hollis had a lot to do.

He was in charge of the autopsy program. He oversaw the entire pathology residency program.

He also directed the second-year pathology course for the medical students.

Dr. Hollis usually covered the weekly Clinicopathologic Conferences (CPCs). CPCs were devilish exercises, which went like this:

A clinician (e.g., internist, surgeon, pediatrician…) was given the pertinent clinical information on a patient who had died – history, physical findings, lab results, the X-rays – everything except the most important thing – the final diagnosis. For fifty minutes or so the clinician discussed the patient's maladies and then rendered final diagnoses – hopefully correct. Then the pathologist, usually Dr. Hollis, demonstrated the autopsy findings.

In addition, each Thursday at noon Dr. Hollis had a conference for the entire pathology house staff, covering ten microscopic slides. On Monday he would put out a set of ten slides next to the microscope in the residents' conference room. The slides were accompanied by a sheet of paper with information about each slide, but of course, no diagnosis. Then on Thursday he would discuss the cases one by one, calling on the residents to describe the findings, and then ask questions in his usual Socratic fashion.

Dr. Hollis also was involved in the care of real live patients, not just patients who had died and those presented at conferences. Previous students and residents sent Dr. Hollis cases that they needed help on. Dr. Hollis looked at the microscopic slides and then phoned the person who sent in the case, and related his impressions and diagnoses of the case.

Southeastern was an academic institution, with visiting professors and experts who gave lectures from time to time, and Dr. Hollis sometimes attended these talks.

One time I asked Dr. Hollis which type of teaching he preferred. Not surprisingly, he answered that he liked teaching the residents the best, because he could cover pathology deeply and relatively completely over four years. He liked teaching medical students, but not quite as much, because the pathology course was only a semester, and it was hard to get too much material covered in just a semester. Finally, Dr. Hollis's least favorite teaching involved the CPCs because he "had to water it down so much."

CHAPTER 25

Maybe CPCs were watered down, but they could be plenty dramatic. They were held in a large amphitheater with tiered seating and a pit at the bottom where the clinician presented the case for discussion. His task was to discuss the findings of the patient, give a differential diagnosis (a list of possible causes/diseases causing the patient's problems), and then make a decision about what the patient died of. Dr. Hollis would then present the pathology findings, which would confirm or refute the clinician's diagnoses.

The seating was as ceremonial as the Roman Coliseum. The lower tiers were reserved for the chairman of the Medicine Department, Dr. Hollis, professors, Nobel laureates, and distinguished visiting physicians. The interns and residents sat behind these dignitaries, and the medical students sat in the remaining upper rows, filling the Coliseum, I mean amphitheater. In the pit the gladiator, I mean presenter, stood behind a podium. He could use the chalkboard at the back of the pit to make his points, and demonstrate the X-ray findings on an X-ray viewing station next to him. From the ceiling a screen came down, on which Dr. Hollis demonstrated the pathology findings by projecting Kodachromes rotating around on the "carousel."

The clinicopathologic conferences were scheduled Fridays at noon, so the attendees brought sack lunches to eat during the hour-long conference. The students in their long white coats and the house staff in their short white coats looked like chickens roosting. They cackled as they studied the mimeographed sheets of paper with the clinical history, physical findings, and laboratory test results, trying to figure out what the correct diagnosis would be. Did the patient die from pituitary failure or tuberculosis of the adrenal gland, or something else?

74

All the while they ate their sack lunches and drank their sodas. Bets were placed; reputations and fortunes were made and lost.

But no one's reputation gained or lost more than the presenter, who would end his discussion with a definitive diagnosis. Dr. Hollis would then present the pathology findings. The presenter would either be right or wrong.

I remember one clinicopathologic conference vividly.

The gladiator, I mean presenter, was an acquaintance of mine, Dr. Marcus Scoville, the chairman of the Internal Medicine Department at Ivory Medical School, where I had graduated. He, of course, did not know or remember me. It wasn't like he was my mentor or anything. He did not remember the name of his "solid" student.

However, Dr. Scoville *was* a mentor to a classmate and friend of mine, Mark Dallas. Mark was doing his internal medicine residency in San Francisco at the time, and Dr. Scoville was monitoring Mark's progress. Dr. Scoville would eventually recruit Mark to a faculty position at Ivory. That worked out well, because Mark is still there as a professor in the Internal Medicine Department. From time to time I see Mark in the airport on the way to some muckety-muck conference where he is one of the speakers.

Dr. Scoville was visiting Southeastern for some muckety-muck-type stuff himself. As part of the visit, he presented a case at the weekly CPC.

That turned out to be a big mistake.

I was interested to see how Dr. Scoville would do. He was an endocrinologist, primarily a researcher, rarely taking care of patients. Nevertheless, he was expected to be conversant in the case he presented. The deceased female patient had adrenal insufficiency (adrenal failure), an endocrine disorder, which should have been right smack-dab in the middle of his area of expertise.

Nevertheless, the presented case was a challenging diagnostic problem, because many disease conditions cause adrenal failure.

First there are indirect causes of adrenal failure; this is a partial list:

1. Diseases of the hypothalamus.

2. Diseases of the pituitary gland.

Second, obviously diseases of the adrenal gland itself can cause adrenal failure. Examples include the following:

1. An infection (e.g., virus, fungus or tuberculosis).

2. A cancer that destroys the adrenal gland.

3. Or most commonly, an autoimmune problem in which the immune system malfunctions and attacks and destroys the adrenal gland.

So Dr. Scoville had quite a challenge to figure out what exactly had caused the demise of this patient. Dr. Hollis would demonstrate the correct diagnosis, so Dr. Scoville's conclusion would be binary, either right or wrong. The crowd sensed blood; it would be thumbs-up or thumbs-down.

Students, residents, and faculty at a medical school are a fickle, narrow-minded lot who do not have any time to spare to read or think of anything that does not pertain to medicine, so we suffer from lack of imagination and depth of character, which makes us easily manipulated and insecure enough to think that getting a diagnosis at a CPC right or wrong makes any difference in the world. It breaks my heart.

The event started out okay. Dr. Richard Bolton, the chairman of the Southeastern Internal Medicine Department, made the introductions. It was a testimonial as much as an introduction. Dr. Bolton listed the Ivy League Schools where Dr. Scoville had received his education and training, and briefly listed some of the more significant discoveries he had made, and listed the honors he had received so far in his career. He finished by listing the many outstanding doctors and researchers who had trained under Dr. Scoville and been his students. My name was not mentioned.

Dr. Bolton sat down, and Dr. Scoville walked to the podium like a relief pitcher taking the mound in the ninth inning, his team ahead by one run, and the other team has the bases loaded with no outs. Then he proceeded to blow it.

Dr. Scoville started out strong with a pretty good joke. He said, "I could feel sorry for myself that I have to present this very challenging CPC involving a patient who died with very puzzling signs and symptoms, but I won't; as my grandmother used to say to me during hard times, 'no matter how bad things get, there is always someone else who has it worse,' and at a CPC that someone else is pretty easy to find."

White jackets and lab coats fluttered in the roost as the crowd cackled and crowed, because in the pit a casual nonchalant air is cultivated and a good joke venerated – a distraction to get away from the tedium of science and medicine and taking care of cranky sick patients.

But it all went downhill after that. Dr. Scoville seemed unsure of himself and was very tentative as he discussed the differential diagnosis of what could have caused this unfortunate patient's symptoms. Perhaps he was spending so much time doing research, in the lab, that there was little time left over to gain the experience needed to make diagnoses on real live patients and take care of them.

Internists like Dr. Scoville, well, they love the process of differential diagnosis, which is on display at a CPC. Differential diagnosis involves making a list of possible diseases and conditions that could explain the patient's signs and symptoms, which, in the case of a CPC, caused the patient's death. What the internist then likes to do, or loves to do, is go through this list and disqualify each entity one by one until only the correct diagnosis remains, kind of like Dr. Sherlock Holmes liked to do – rule out the impossible until one has to accept the remaining possibility, however improbable.

That approach might have worked for Sherlock Holmes, but it does not work out very well for internists, in my opinion. For Dr. Scoville this approach was a disaster. Where the concept goes wrong, I think, is that by some perversity in thinking by internists, the longer the differential diagnosis, the better. Good to be complete goes the thinking of overrated individuals like Dr. Gregory House. This is preposterous. The shorter the differential diagnosis, the better, in my opinion, with the best differential diagnosis being one diagnosis on one line – the correct diagnosis.

The correct diagnosis was not what Dr. Scoville came up with. After a meandering, poorly reasoned presentation lasting a long fifty minutes, he came up with a diagnosis that I cannot remember, except to know that whatever diagnosis he rendered was incorrect. What I *can* remember, for sure, is that he finished up by saying that he had never seen a case of metastatic carcinoma to both adrenal glands causing these kinds of adrenal problems, so the diagnosis certainly could not be metastatic carcinoma to both adrenal glands, and that there was no way such a thing could have caused the death of this patient.

Unfortunately Dr. Scoville was dead wrong. Metastatic carcinoma to both adrenal glands was precisely what had caused the adrenal failure that killed this patient.

Dr. Bolton introduced Dr. Hollis, saying the pathologist would have all the answers.

As he walked to the pit with his loping gait, Dr. Hollis said in his cowboy twang, "Well, I do have a lot of data."

Which Dr. Hollis presented, including the photographs of metastatic breast cancer replacing the adrenal glands, and the photomicrographs demonstrating how the cancer looked under the microscope as it destroyed the adrenal glands, leading to adrenal failure, which killed the patient. The *click, click, click* of the carousel was like sniper fire interrupting the sober "just the facts" delivery of Dr. Hollis. When he finished, Dr. Hollis sat down.

Students and house staff have no use for weakness in others, being so insecure themselves. They were uncomfortable, looking around, fidgeting with their pencils. So was the faculty. So was everyone. No one looked at Dr. Scoville.

There wasn't much to say after such humiliation. Dr. Scoville stood up and said to the fickle flock, "Now I have seen my first case of adrenal failure secondary to metastatic carcinoma." He sat down, and the restless crowd departed, quiet, like leaving a funeral service.

I was in shock. It reminds me of the great movie *Layer Cake* starring Daniel Craig, back in 2004, before he hit it big with his James Bond gig. Check it out. Dr. Scoville was at the top of the layer cake. He had started out at the bottom of the layer cake, as a medical student, then was a resident, just like me, doing a lot of scut work and taking a lot of shit from everybody, just like me. Then he worked his way up the levels of the layer cake – instructor, assistant professor, associate professor, full professor, and then chairman of the Medicine Department, where he was at the top of the layer cake and didn't have to take shit from anyone. But he did. I had just seen him make a fool of himself, which was not exactly taking shit from somebody, but pretty darn close. If Dr. Scoville – a legend, a giant – could be humiliated in such a way, what hope was there for the rest of us? What hope was there for me?

CHAPTER 26

I was reviewing slides with Dr. Hollis. We sat across from each other, looking through a double-headed microscope, each seeing the same thing. It was a Friday. We talked about the college football games happening the next day, and bemoaned the fact that the Texas-Oklahoma game was blacked out on TV, because Oklahoma was on NCAA probation for one thing or another and ineligible to have its games televised. This was a shame, because that year Texas and Oklahoma were two of the best teams in the country.

Dr. Hollis's small refrigerator hummed in the background. He slid his chair over to the fridge and grabbed a six-ounce bottle of Coca-Cola. He asked me if I wanted one. I did. Six-ounce Cokes are the best product this venerable company makes, in my opinion.

The autopsy slides we were examining were from the right cerebellum part of the brain, a site of massive bleeding that had killed the patient. That part of the case was obvious.

However, the source of the bleeding and cause of the bleeding were not obvious and were not well defined at all during the patient's short hospital stay, although X-ray studies had raised the possibility of an arteriovenous malformation.

Like most things in medicine, arteriovenous malformations are poorly understood. Arteries and veins are fairly easy to differentiate from each other under the microscope. Arteries carry blood from the heart, so they have higher pressure to contend with: therefore they tend to have thicker walls and some specialized anatomy to deal with the stresses of the pressure. Veins, on the other hand, have less pressure to contend with, because by the time the blood has reached the veins, it has traversed capillaries and tissues, which damp down the pressure. Therefore veins tend to have thinner walls and a relatively simple anatomy. With a little practice, it's easy to differentiate arteries from veins.

Arteriovenous malformations, as the name implies, do not have the organized anatomy of either arteries or veins, but are a haphazard collection of vessels with disorganized anatomy. These vessels are so abnormal that they do not do a good job of keeping blood where it is supposed to be. For example, some parts of the arteriovenous malformation have walls that are too thin or irregular to do the job of transporting blood, so that the blood does not stay where it is supposed to be, in the vessel, but bleeds out with resultant hemorrhage.

The massive hemorrhage that killed this patient obscured the lesion that had caused the bleeding. An arteriovenous malformation was only a possible explanation, not a definitive diagnosis. As if the patient's problems were not complex enough, the neurosurgeons had done an operation to remove the blood from the cerebellum to try to relieve the pressure on the brain. This attempt to save the patient's life unfortunately was unsuccessful. But, when they were doing this operation, did the neurosurgeons remove the arteriovenous malformation, which may or may not have existed? No one knew.

In summary, the patient's hospital course was a complicated mess, and the clinicians sure wanted to know what had happened.

It was up to me to find out. Actually, it was up to Dr. Hollis, because so far I had failed to find evidence for or against the diagnosis of arteriovenous malformation – not for lack of trying. When I performed the autopsy, the right cerebellum was pretty much destroyed, replaced by blood, and it was impossible to determine the source of the bleeding. I submitted this zone of hemorrhage for microscopic examination, hoping that what I was unable to identify with the naked eye would be visible with the microscope. However, my microscopic examination revealed a lot of blood and some residual cerebellum tissue, but no arteriovenous malformation. I assumed then that the neurosurgeons had removed the arteriovenous malformation during their operation. I didn't particularly like that explanation, but that was where I was.

Dr. Hollis and I looked at the slides of the cerebellum. He worked fast, putting a slide on the stage, examining it thoroughly but quickly, then taking it off the stage, putting it in the slide folder, picking up the next one and examining it. We saw a lot of blood, a little cerebellum.

Then suddenly he twisted the focusing knob rapidly so that the image was out of focus. He leaned back and said, "What we are looking for is very subtle, right? I mean the radiologists weren't even sure an arteriovenous malformation was there?"

"Yes," I said.

"We need to keep that in mind as we look at these slides."

He leaned forward again and focused the microscope, to reveal...an arteriovenous malformation. It was small, barely filling a few fields at very high magnification, but it was there alright – a mishmash of vessels with walls of varying thicknesses, neither artery nor vein, some thin, some thick, and everything in between. The vessels had irregular contours as well. Overall it was a mishmash, a mess, and was the obvious cause of the hemorrhage.

How had I missed it? It was hard to find, present in one small area of one slide, out of about fifteen slides of the area.

But missed it I had, and I felt terrible.

Dr. Eisen, the department's liver and kidney pathologist, came in just as Dr. Hollis was about to chew me out. I liked Dr. Eisen. He was an excellent tennis player, and we played about once a month. He almost always beat me. "Am I interrupting anything?" he asked.

"I'd be hard-pressed to think of a worse time," I said.

"Sorry," he said, smiling. "I was attending a roundtable with a bunch of forensic pathologists, and we discussed the best way to die. After all, they should know. They all wanted to be shot in the back when they were 103 years old, by a jealous husband."

Dr. Eisen left, and I guess Dr. Hollis liked the joke, because he forgot to chew me out. We looked at the next slide.

There are three take-home points in this episode:

1. How easy he made it look. The true artists, the geniuses, in any field make it look easy. This is most noticeable in sports – Arthur Ashe in tennis, Nolan Ryan in baseball, and Michael Jordon in basketball (baseball not so much). I saw Arthur Ashe in person the year he won almost all the major tournaments, including Wimbledon. He was in a zone that year, hitting

great shot after great shot, dominating whomever he played. I saw Nolan Ryan pitch several times in his prime; his warm-up pitches were faster than most pitchers' game pitches, and when the game started, I could barely see his fastball, let alone catch it or hit it. I saw Michael Jordan play against the Atlanta Hawks when he was playing for the Chicago Bulls. He was faster and quicker than anyone on the floor, by far; it was like everyone else was playing in slow motion. Dr. Hollis was like this. He could take any botched dissection, disorganized presentation, or in this case, a subtle microscopic lesion, and make everything come together and make sense. And make it look easy.

2. He taught me what I needed to know. I missed my first arteriovenous malformation, but since that time I have diagnosed hundreds, maybe thousands of arteriovenous malformations, which can show up in other organs in the body, not just the brain/cerebellum. They can show up in many places – the skin, subcutaneous fat, soft tissue, kidney, gastrointestinal tract – pretty much anywhere. To my knowledge, since this first one in the cerebellum, I have missed nary a one. It's not a particularly easy straightforward diagnosis, but I have made it many times and correlated it with the signs and symptoms of the patient. Sometimes the arteriovenous malformation showed up with bleeding, as this one did, but other times it just showed up as a mass. Several times when I have made this diagnosis for a surgeon, the surgeon has an "aha" moment, and says, "In retrospect, that fits what I saw." That may not be much, but in my desert of a life, moments like those are oases.

3. The patience of the man. It has to be hard to be brilliant, to be a genius, because others can't keep up. Think of it – having to explain the same things over and over, sometimes to the same persons over and over. It must be like walking up a hill of sand, slowly and laboriously. But maybe not. Maybe part of being a genius is recognizing the fact that certain things come easier to the genius than to others. Perhaps a genius perceives the presence of a gift that most do not have, and have the em-

pathy to teach others anyway. Nevertheless, when I messed up, I think Dr. Hollis was hurt, really hurt, that in spite of his teaching I could make such an error. Part of his gift to me, and the rest of his students and residents, was his patience.

One more thing, not about Dr. Hollis, but about me: This illustrates why I did what I did those four years, why I put up with the insults and challenges put to me by Dr. Hollis (and there were others similar to him on the Southeastern Pathology faculty, but this book is not about them). Pathology itself was fun. For example, in this case of the cerebellar arteriovenous malformation, I, well, we, discovered the answer to the question – what caused this patient's demise? If I kept working and studying, I would learn more, and I could do this on my own. I could learn enough to be able to answer questions from clinicians and patients about what was causing the disease and pain they were witnessing. I would know the answers and be able to help them. And to me that was not only something noble, but interesting, and the most wonderful thing imaginable.

See, the hours I spent reading and learning, looking through the microscope, examining tissues, attending lectures – that wasn't work, it was fun. It was a privilege to learn how the body works, and what could go wrong, and the science of how that happened. I would have done it for no pay whatsoever. It did not seem particularly strenuous; it was something I enjoyed. I even had this crazy idea that I had some talent, which no one, especially Dr. Hollis, had discerned, but maybe someday someone would. Maybe even Dr. Hollis.

CHAPTER 27

Dr. Hollis's commandment "you can't not know" was applied to his second-year medical students, future physicians, but even more so to his interns and residents, future pathologists. Dr. Hollis's thinking was that physicians, clinicians, would send specimens to pathologists for answers, for diagnoses, so that they would know how to treat the patient and make the patient's pain go away. A neurosurgeon sends a portion of a patient's brain mass to a pathologist and wants to know what the lesion is – a tumor, abscess, or something else. And if the brain mass is a tumor, what kind of tumor. Similarly, a general surgeon will send a breast biopsy to a pathologist to determine whether it is benign or malignant, with drastically different follow-ups depending on the diagnosis. A thoracic surgeon sends a lung specimen to a pathologist to see if the lesion is a tumor or an inflammatory process, and if inflammatory, what is causing the inflammation – tuberculosis, fungus infection, allergic reaction, or something else – so that appropriate treatment can be given to the patient. An internal medicine specialist, let's say a gastroenterologist, sends a liver biopsy or colon biopsy for interpretation and diagnosis. The list of examples is endless, but here's one more: an interventional radiologist uses complicated equipment to help him stick a needle into a pancreas or lung or liver of a patient, with obvious hassle and discomfort to the patient, for the sole purpose of getting some tissue for a pathologist to examine and make a diagnosis – that's the whole point.

Therefore, Dr. Hollis's thinking was that for pathologists, even more than for most physicians, there were extraordinary expectations. Dr. Hollis's mantra "you can't not know" meant to Dr. Hollis that a pathologist had to know as much gynecology as a gynecologist, as much medicine as an internist, as much general surgery as a surgeon…and also know everything about the specialty of pathology.

So:

1. We pathologists were to know as much about acute appendicitis as a general surgeon – causes, anatomy, treatment…and also know pathology.

2. We pathologists were to know as much about diabetes as an internist – causes, related biochemistry, treatment, complications…and also know pathology.

3. We pathologists were to know as much about cervical cancer as a gynecologist – epidemiology, causes, how to treat it – and also know pathology.

I think the reader gets the point.

How is that possible?

Of course, it isn't possible. So Dr. Hollis conceded that there were some details of treatment a pathologist did not need to know. For example, a pathologist did not have to know exactly what kind of sutures needed to be used in an operation to remove an appendix. A pathologist did not have to know the exact doses of drugs used to treat diabetes. Nor did a pathologist need to know the details of how a gynecologist did colposcopy to carefully examine the cervix.

There was no sharp line about what to know or not know. Some details of treatment we did have to know – like the effects of various medications on organs, or the possible complications of various operations. Also, Dr. Hollis expected us to know pros and cons about various treatment alternatives, like whether medical treatment or surgery was better for an entity such as arteriosclerosis of the carotid arteries.

In summary, other than some details of treatment, we pathology interns and residents were to learn everything our fellow clinical residents learned during their surgical and medical training…and become experts in pathology.

CHAPTER 28

We were studying a brain. When it comes out of the body, the brain is too soft to examine. It is a grayish white soft structure with a consistency unique in my experience, somewhere between a paste and a gel – so soft that I can no longer stand boxing, which used to be one of my favorite sports to watch. Muhammad Ali was another genius in his field, who made it look easy. At this point though, watching the blows to the head that occur during a boxing match, and visualizing what it does to the brain, well, I just can't take it. After viewing Dr. Bennett Omalu's work as dramatized by the movie *Concussion*, my football watching days are decreasing as well and may stop.

The brain, being so soft, has to "fix" for several days in formalin to make it firm enough to examine. Sometimes Dr. Hollis deferred this brain examination work to the neuropathologist on staff, but the case that day was so interesting he wanted to supervise the brain dissection himself.

Indeed, the outlook for some interesting findings was excellent. The elderly woman patient had died of a stroke, specifically a brain infarct, which means part of the brain had died, presumably from lack of blood supply. I thought the cause of this lack of blood was a thrombus (clot) in the right posterior inferior cerebellar artery, which led to a brain infarct involving the right cerebellum with resultant characteristic signs and symptoms, and caused death by involvement of the adjacent brainstem, which controls important body functions, like breathing. I said all this as I answered Dr. Hollis's questions.

Then we examined the brain. We opened the right posterior inferior cerebellar artery, and there was the prettiest soft grayish tan thrombus (clot) you ever did see, just as I had predicted. We examined the right cerebellum and adjacent brainstem, which did not "fix" as it was supposed to in the formalin, but had a soft tan mushy appearance, clearly different from the adjacent normal tissues – classic dead brain tissue (an infarct) just as I had predicted. "You done good," said Dr. Hollis.

After the examination of the brain was complete, and the diagnoses had been made, and photographs taken, and appropriate samples submitted for microscopic examination – we played one of Dr. Hollis's favorite games: "The brain game." Dr. Hollis thought that his pathology residents should know neuroanatomy as well as neurosurgeons, neurologists, or for that matter, anyone – as well as know pathology. So to make this happen, he played the brain game, which went like this:

Hollis excused all the residents and anyone else who was present. While they were gone, Dr. Hollis sectioned the brain into small parts – cubes, triangles, squares – and then lined them up on the cutting board. Dr. Hollis then put a pin with a red head into a neuroanatomic structure to mark it, e.g., hippocampus, optic chiasm, anterior commissure, globus pallidus, and pretty much any other identifiable part of the brain. The "game" was for the resident to identify the structure marked by the pin. In order not to look stupid, that meant that the last thing I had to do the night before a brain session was to review neuroanatomy as illustrated in a book titled *Atlas of the Human Brain in Section*, an eighty-five-page book I had memorized.

I held my own in the brain game. I "done good."

CHAPTER 29

No one was immune from interrogations by Dr. Hollis. A visiting professor, a world-famous infectious disease specialist, was visiting Southeastern, and he had heard about Dr. Hollis's teaching methods. He wanted to see firsthand how he conducted an autopsy review.

The review proceeded in the usual way. During the patient's clinical course, he had some unexplained kidney problems, which were never diagnosed with any certainty, and the biggest reason the autopsy was done was to get a definitive anatomic diagnosis of the cause of the patent's abnormal renal function.

Since the kidneys were the key organs, they were the last ones to be reviewed. The kidneys had small well-circumscribed white dots scattered throughout the tissue, easily seen on the cut surfaces. Dr. Hollis placed the kidneys on the cutting board, and he decided to play another one of his favorite games: "All will look and all will write."

It was a simple game. Dr. Hollis handed out pieces of paper; everyone looked at the organ in question, wrote down a diagnosis, and signed the document. Dr. Hollis then reviewed the submitted diagnoses one by one, noting why each diagnosis was correct or not. Of course, the "correct" diagnosis was whatever Dr. Hollis said it was, and then he closed out the session with his reasoning of how he came to his diagnosis.

Like I said, a simple game.

But evidently too complicated for the visiting professor. Everyone, all the residents and interns, wrote down their diagnoses and handed the papers to Dr. Hollis. That is everyone except the visiting world-famous infectious disease specialist. So Dr. Hollis repeated, "*All* will look and all will write."

Finally the visiting professor wrote out his diagnosis and handed it to Dr. Hollis.

Everyone, including the world-famous expert, got the answer wrong – except for Dr. Hollis, who correctly recognized that the lesions were caused by *Candida albicans*, which is a fungus known to cause characteristic white dots anyplace they infect, including the kidney.

CHAPTER 30

On December 31 I ended my six-month rotation on the autopsy service. That morning I reviewed microscopic slides of a case with Dr. Hollis. I was in a great mood, just to be through with it. Dr. Hollis seemed cheerful as well, probably happy to get me off his service.

Actually he encouraged me. Dr. Hollis said that I had made a lot of progress, that I now knew the technique of doing an autopsy, and that I had a good base of knowledge on which to build – not much of an endorsement, but enough for me. I was just glad I'd survived.

CHAPTER 31

The next day, January 1, I started my chemistry rotation. But that didn't mean I was done with autopsies. I had to finish the autopsies I had performed during the month of December and even before that. So for weeks I looked at the autopsy slides, went over the slides with Dr. Hollis or the faculty member who was assigned the case, and completed paperwork – always more paperwork.

Obviously I worked on these unfinished autopsy cases during some of the time I should have been learning chemistry, which meant my chemistry duties were not getting all the attention they deserved. But that's the way it was at the Southeastern Pathology Department. Anatomic pathology (autopsy pathology and surgical pathology) had priority over clinical pathology (chemistry, microbiology, blood banking, and hematology).

After the leisurely pace of chemistry, things picked up again during my six-month surgical pathology rotation. I examined specimens from real live patients, so the stakes in patient-care terms were much higher than the stakes during the autopsy service. Let's face it, the stakes on the autopsy service were so high because Dr. Hollis was so intense; the stakes weren't so high for the patient – the patient was dead.

On the surgical pathology service, I along with other residents on the service did the dissection of all the specimens:

1. Big – colon resections, gastrectomies, mastectomies...

2. And small – skin biopsies, cervical biopsies, appendectomies...

The day after the dissections, the microscopic slides of the specimens I had examined were given to me to look at. Then I reviewed them with one of the faculty surgical pathologists. Then I did the paperwork. Always paperwork.

Three months of hematology followed. That rotation was similar to surgical pathology, except the only kinds of specimens I looked at were bone marrows, lymph nodes, spleens, and other hematology-type specimens.

CHAPTER 32

Just because I was off the autopsy service, doing these other rotations, did not mean I was free of Dr. Hollis's influence. I saw him at least once a week at his weekly Thursday noon slide conference.

On Mondays, next to a microscope in the Residents' Conference Room, Dr. Hollis put out ten slides to review, with a piece of paper relating brief information about each slide. When I say brief, I mean very brief, like one or two sentences or less, something like "forty-five-year-old woman" or "brain biopsy." Any information that would actually aid in the diagnosis was withheld. For example, Dr. Hollis would put out a slide with a history of "liver biopsy," and the liver biopsy would demonstrate a malignant tumor; what Dr. Hollis would *not* relate to us was that the patient had a previously diagnosed lung cancer. That would have made a diagnosis of lung cancer metastatic to the liver too easy, and Dr. Hollis did not want anything for us to be too easy.

I think there is merit in that approach. Robert D. Kaplan in his book *Hog Pilots, Blue Water Grunts* describes a submarine military exercise deliberately made very challenging with multiple objectives – laying mines, getting attacked at the same time by two enemy warships, thus having to fire torpedoes –way beyond anything likely to occur in real combat. The point of the exercise was that when they were actually called upon to do a real mission, it would be easy.

Dr. Hollis took a similar approach to his residents. By challenging us to make diagnoses on limited material and limited information, his thinking was that when we got to the real practice of pathology, with plenty of tissue and plenty of clinical information – our jobs would be easy.

94

So Monday morning until Thursday noon, we residents looked at the slides, tried to make correct diagnoses, and then studied about the disease the slide demonstrated. We needed to be ready to discuss each case. Thursday noon was showtime. It was a lot of work. No one wanted to look foolish.

It was a game, really, to see how much of a diagnosis can be made doing a microscopic examination with little or no clinical information. But for us the stakes were very high. We all wanted to be prepared so we would look good in front of Dr. Hollis and our peers. Our futures were at stake. The exercise made us look hard, really hard, at the slide to glean as much information as possible.

Actually the slide conference was good training for what would happen when we went out to practice on our own. I never did get into a situation where I had all of the tissue I wanted and all the clinical information I needed. During my career, I have received countless specimens with little or no history. Worse yet, sometimes the history that was given was wrong, e.g., skin biopsy submitted from a "*3 year old*" patient showed a malignant melanoma so rare as to be reportable – only to find out "there was a clerical mistake; we meant to write *30 year old* patient." So, perhaps unintentionally, the challenging nature of the conference was good training for real pathology practice.

Dr. Hollis's Thursday conference began punctually at noon and lasted an hour. All the residents, whatever service they were on, took a break to attend the conference. The week gradually built up to the conference, which was the climax of the week, and when it was over, to an amazing extent the week was over. Everybody exhaled.

The meeting took place in a small classroom. The chief resident stood at the back of the room, projecting the microscopic images on to a screen at the front of the room. Dr. Hollis sat in the front of the room with the residents seated in a semicircle facing him, ready for questions. The lights were off so that the projected images could be seen on the screen. The resultant dim lighting and shadows gave the room a surreal chiaroscuro appearance. As we looked at the projected images of the microscopic slides, Dr. Hollis asked one of the residents to describe the findings. Once the microscopic appearance of the lesion was thoroughly described, Dr. Hollis asked for the resident's diagnosis of the case. Dr. Hollis would then ask more questions, which would elicit more answers, which would lead to more questions. The teaching was Socratic.

Under such conditions, it was easy for a resident to look foolish. When that happened, everyone in the room hooted, laughed, and hollered – everyone except the person who made the mistake. The situation was this: Dr. Hollis was the leader of a pack of wolves prowling for weak prey, which could be attacked and devoured.

Nothing made Dr. Hollis happier than to try to talk a resident out of a correct diagnosis. Here are a couple of examples:

1. The history Dr. Hollis relates is a seventy-one-year-old male who died of a myocardial infarct (i.e., heart attack). The slide shows a colon cancer (specifically an adenocarcinoma), not a great example, but still a cancer.

    Resident: My diagnosis is adenocarcinoma of the colon.

    Dr. Hollis: I may not have made this clear, but the cause of death in this patient was a myocardial infarct. The patient was in the intensive care unit, recovering from a heart attack. There was no mention of colon cancer whatsoever in the chart. This was an *incidental* finding at autopsy, totally unrelated to any symptoms the patient had.

    Resident: It's still a cancer.

    DR. Hollis: You are making a very significant diagnosis, a cancer, which untreated kills a patient in less than a year, and you are making this diagnosis as an incidental finding, a lethal disease that did not cause the death of the patient!? Extraordinary. I have never heard of such a thing.

    Resident: You have now.

2. The history is that the patient has a history of a dermoid cyst of the right ovary. The slide in question is of the left ovary. It has a dermoid cyst as well.

    Resident: My diagnosis is dermoid cyst.

Dr. Hollis: But the patient already had a dermoid cyst on the right.

Resident: Well, it happens. Dermoid cysts can be bilateral.

Dr. Hollis: You are telling me dermoid cysts can be bilateral!?

Resident: My diagnosis is dermoid cyst.

Dr. Hollis: Well, I guess I'm not as experienced as you are, because I have never seen such a thing. I thought it was pretty neat.

The obvious lesson: when you are confident of your diagnosis, stand your ground.

If a resident and Dr. Hollis disagreed on a diagnosis, the lights came on and Dr. Hollis stepped to the blackboard. The resident would state the reasons favoring his diagnosis. Dr. Hollis wrote these reasons in very small letters. Then Dr. Hollis would state the reasons he favored his diagnosis, and as he did, he wrote his reasons in very big bold letters. At the conclusion of this exercise Dr. Hollis related the definitive diagnosis – based on clinical follow-up, additional tissue, special stains or studies – something definitive that solved the case.

Of course, the additional information invariably confirmed Dr. Hollis's diagnosis.

One of my better moments was at this conference. The microscopic slide for review demonstrated a brain tumor. Dr. Hollis called on resident after resident, trying to pry a correct diagnosis out of someone, without success. He pointed out the flaws of each resident's diagnosis. When the resident couldn't refute Dr. Hollis's comments, he moved on and questioned another resident.

For some reason, I *knew* that the tumor of the brain was a reticulum cell sarcoma. I have no idea how I knew that, but I did. Dr. Hollis skipped a few residents and jumped over to me to ask me my interpretations of the lesion. I told him it was a reticulum cell sarcoma and why.

"Right."

Reticulum cell sarcoma in the brain was a rare diagnosis in the 1970s, but it's nonexistent now. Oh, the disease entity, this tumor of the brain, still exists, but it's not called reticulum cell sarcoma anymore. What we now know, decades later, is that reticulum sarcoma was a "wastebasket diagnosis," which means several different kinds of tumors were called this entity. Now the tumors we used to classify as "reticulum cell sarcomas" have been reclassified and renamed various types of other malignant tumors, which type depending on the results of special studies like flow cytometry, immunohistochemistry stains, and other studies in addition to routine histology. So what pathologists used to call reticulum cell sarcoma is now designated one of ninety subtypes of malignant lymphoma and various other malignant tumors, each with its own characteristics and recommended treatment. But in the 1970s when routine microscopic examination was about all we had, the diagnosis was reticulum cell sarcoma.

We had a veterinary pathologist on staff, Dr. Shale, who attended Dr. Hollis's conference. Often he added one of his cases to the conference and put out microscopic slides of some critter for us to examine. They were tough cases. It's hard enough to diagnose diseases in humans, but in a different species, it's almost impossible. What looks benign in a dog is actually malignant, and what looks malignant is actually benign. Dr. Shale, a kind man, would then gently correct us and teach us something.

Dr. Hollis had a bulldog named Brute. Dr. Hollis loved that dog and delighted in extolling Brute's exploits as he terrorized and intimidated cats and other dogs. One such tale involved Brute whipping a porcupine in a fair fight, during a ski trip to New Mexico. When he returned to Southeastern, Dr. Hollis gave anyone who would listen a blow-by-blow account of the battle. Dr. Hollis did concede, however, that a veterinarian had to remove some porcupine quills from the skin of the victorious Brute.

Shortly thereafter, Dr. Shale put out a slide from the "skin of a dog" for review at Dr. Hollis's conference. It showed an inflammatory lesion consistent with inflammation from a porcupine quill. It didn't take Sherlock Holmes to deduce that the "skin of a dog" was in fact skin from Brute, and the inflammation was a battle scar from the porcupine fight.

So we residents showed up at the conference ready to show off our brilliant conclusions. When we got to that case, Dr. Shale called on various residents to describe and diagnose the lesion. Everyone came up with the same diagnosis – inflammation secondary to a porcupine quill, and each one speculated that it came from the skin of Brute, noting that Dr. Hollis's dog had recently been involved in a battle with a porcupine, and that even though Brute had prevailed, he had received this injury in the process. Dr. Hollis smiled and nodded his head up and down proudly as his dog's heroic deeds were recounted again and again. Finally, Dr. Shale asked if there was *any* resident who had a different diagnosis?

No.

We were all wrong. Dr. Shale demonstrated that lesion was a mast cell tumor, quite common in dogs, not inflammation from a porcupine quill.

The end result was that Dr. Hollis got to relive the *Brute and the Porcupine* adventure, without saying a word.

CHAPTER 33

House staff were chattel. There were no limitations on working hours or working conditions as there are today. There were no resident "councils" with input about how to make things better and more helpful to the house staff. At Southeastern if I or any of the other residents made any complaints, we would have been laughed out of the program. Actually, we would not have been laughed out; instead, our year-to-year contracts would not be renewed.

We didn't care about any of that. We pathology residents wanted to work hard, to push ourselves to the limit, and become good pathologists. It was a total surrender. We gave up time with our families and free time to study and work. We jeopardized our health and well-being. There was an esprit de corps, all of us pushing each other to our limits.

Into this setting came Dr. Darrell Hollis, a man with all the answers, the smartest man I ever met, who said, "You can't not know."

There had to be an endgame that each us would get to the point where we would not not know, that we *would* know and have all the answers.

Dr. Metcalf was obviously such a person, who had all the answers. He was a visiting professor who came to Southeastern each winter, to get away from the cold winters in Boston, where he was on the medical staff of Massachusetts General Hospital. He was a roly-poly man with pale skin and white hair, a smiling pleasant demeanor, and a kind countenance. Sol Steinberg, my best friend among the residents, said that Dr. Metcalf and his wife looked like Mr. and Mrs. Santa Claus.

If anyone had reached the top layer of the pathology layer cake, it was Dr. Metcalf. He was on the faculty of an Ivy League medical school. He was the world's expert on thyroid gland pathology. He wrote a book, *Tumors of the Thyroid*, for the Armed forces Institute of Pathology, and he was the chairman of the World Health Organization's task force on classification of thyroid tumors.

One time Dr. Metcalf attended Dr. Hollis's weekly slide conference. As Dr. Metcalf entered, Dr. Hollis acknowledged his presence.

"Most of you know Dr. Metcalf," said Dr. Hollis. "For those of you who don't, in addition to being the world's expert on thyroid gland pathology, he is an expert in all areas of surgical pathology; I do not know of a finer surgical pathologist than Dr. Metcalf."

Dr. Metcalf took his seat in a humble fashion. Addressing Dr. Hollis, he said, "Thank you for those kind words."

Then Dr. Metcalf addressed the residents: "Of course, you do not need to believe everything Dr. Hollis says."

"Oh yes we do," said one of the residents.

By a strange coincidence, which would not be believable if this were fiction, the first case was a thyroid tumor. It was not a microscopic slide, but a photograph of a thyroid gland, which was projected onto the screen. The image showed an obvious tumor. The challenge was to discern, from the photograph alone, whether the tumor was benign or malignant. Dr. Hollis regarded as an indispensable skill that a pathologist be able to diagnose a specimen based on its naked-eye appearance (macroscopic appearance) without the aid of a microscope (microscopic appearance). "The microscopic exam is just to confirm the diagnoses based on the macroscopic examination," he often said.

Of course, at a Dr. Hollis event, everyone was fair game. He asked Dr. Metcalf to discuss the specimen. It was a tough case. The photograph showed an obvious tumor mass, a gray zone clearly different from the homogenous reddish brown thyroid gland tissue in the background. However, it was extremely challenging to determine, from the photograph alone, whether it was benign or malignant. Benign tumors tend to be sharply demarcated from the adjacent thyroid gland, often with a distinct obvious capsule, a band of white fibrous tissue, like a scar, surrounding the benign tumor. In contrast, the demarcation of a malignant tumor and the normal thyroid is not sharp at all, as the malignant tumor invades the normal thyroid, and if there is a capsule, it is invaded as well.

Well, this lesion was neither fish nor fowl. For the most part the mass was circumscribed, with a well-defined capsule, but there was a focal zone, about half an inch or so, where the tumor appeared to invade into the thyroid gland, but this was a subtle change. Tough case.

Dr. Metcalf got off to a shaky start. He had not seen the picture ahead of time. "It's a thyroid gland," he said.

Then he was quiet as he studied the features of the lesion. The quiet could not have lasted that long, but it seemed long enough to dash all my hopes and dreams, and those of everyone in the room. The image stayed on the screen. Dr. Metcalf continued to study it. The tension in the room rose like an episode of *the Twilight Zone.*

Why? Here's why. After Dr. Metcalf made his diagnosis, the correct answer would follow. The microscopic findings, additional clinical findings, or something would definitively prove whether this tumor was benign or malignant, and whether Dr. Metcalf was right or wrong. We residents really wanted him to be right. Because if Dr. Metcalf got it wrong, there was no hope for the rest of us. I mean, it was one thing for ignorant inexperienced pathologists in training like us to mess up, make mistakes, and get things wrong. But good heavens, Dr. Metcalf was a brilliant pathologist, the world's expert on the thyroid gland. If he messed up, everything we residents were working for would be called into question. What kept us going was believing that there had to be an endgame, that as we went up the layer cake, taking shit and abuse along the way, that somehow, someday, we would know what we were doing, and we would reach the top of the layer cake and never have to take shit or abuse ever again. Had to. We would be like Dr. Metcalf. So if a giant like Dr. Metcalf couldn't reach the top of the layer cake, who could? He had to make the correct diagnosis. Had to. It was an existential moment.

He made the correct diagnosis. "There is some capsular invasion at that one edge," said Dr. Metcalf. "My diagnosis is malignant tumor."

Dr. Hollis projected the microscopic slides proving that the thyroid lesion was indeed a malignant tumor.

The harmony and order in the universe were intact.

CHAPTER 34

My three-month rotation at the Veterans Administration Hospital (VA) started in January, midway through my second year of residency, and lasted three months. It was notable for a couple of things:

1. I did a lot of surgical pathology, looking at specimens. It was a big hospital, and most days the only pathologists available to do the work were me and one VA staff pathologist who didn't want to be there. He was waiting for a job opening at the most prestigious private hospital in town and hated the VA. He left about noon, and I pretty much handled whatever happened after that, which was a lot of work, but also a lot of experience. I was only midway into my second year, and most residents didn't do this relatively independent rotation until their fourth year. When I rotated off the service, there was no resident to take my place, and the attending was on his own for a while. He was overwhelmed and told me, "I didn't realize all the work you did."

2. One day a week, however, Dr. Metcalf, the visiting professor from Boston, the world's expert on the thyroid gland, came to the VA as a visiting consultant and reviewed specimens with me. I enjoyed working with him and was sorry to see our collaboration end, but at the end of the three months, it was time for me leave the VA and go on to my next rotation, and for Dr. Metcalf to return to Boston. As we finished our last session at the two-headed microscope, he said, "You have a good eye. When you are good at something, it makes you want to do more of it, and when you do more of it, the better you get. It's a nice cycle."

The compliment that I had a "good eye" was huge. To say a pathologist has a "good eye" means that pathologist has the talent, the knack – an unteachable skill that enables one to look through a microscope and make diagnoses. A person either has a good eye or he doesn't.

The term "right stuff" conveys a similar concept. In his book *The Right Stuff*, Tom Wolfe writes about whether or not an airplane pilot has the "right stuff," an ineffable something, more than training or experience, that enables a pilot to get his plane back on the ground safely, no matter what happens. Those qualities were best exemplified by Chuck Yeager, legendary flying ace and test pilot, who absolutely had the right stuff.

Dr. Metcalf saying to me that I had a "good eye" was like Chuck Yeager telling a cadet he had the right stuff.

Dr. Metcalf believed in me, the first one.

CHAPTER 35

With those words of encouragement behind me, I returned to Southeastern for a three-month rotation on blood banking.

More importantly, at this time in my training, nearing the end of my second year, I began moonlighting at the Medical Examiner's Office in a nearby city, working as a deputy chief medical examiner. As long as anyone could remember, there was a history and tradition that two residents from Southeastern did this job.

Chad Sharon, a third-year resident, got me the job. He was alternating every other weekend with Lloyd Wagner, a fourth-year resident. Lloyd was finishing up his residency and going into military service, so Chad asked me to take Lloyd's place. The job consisted of doing forensic autopsies, or if an autopsy was not needed, doing external exams of deceased persons, and of course dictating our findings and conclusions. My boss was the chief medical examiner, Dr. Musial. My first Saturday at work I got an official card with my title of deputy chief medical examiner.

I was thrilled and honored to get this opportunity. The pay was pretty good, a hundred dollars a day, which in the 1970s was a lot of money. I was only earning one thousand dollars a month at Southeastern.

The job was kind of a secret though. Dr. Page, the chairman of the department, did not approve of the job. In fact, he did not approve of any kind of moonlighting job. His opinion was that his residents should be devoted to learning pathology skills at Southeastern, which did not allow time for moonlighting.

I thought this was preposterous. Moonlighting at the Medical Examiner's Office gave me tremendous amounts of experience, in *pathology*. Many of the autopsies were done for medical conditions –

sudden death from hemorrhage from a lung cancer, myocardial infarcts, intracerebral hemorrhage, and numerous other disease states. And the true forensic-type autopsies – gunshot wounds, suicides, auto accidents, and the like, well, that was pathology too, and forensic pathology experience that I would not get at Southeastern.

Chad and I had no doubt that Dr. Page knew that we were doing medical examiners work – good heavens, this practice had been going on for decades before us. It was a don't ask, don't tell arrangement.

I sure did get a lot of experience. Not only did I cover every other weekend, but Dr. Musial was born and raised in Hungary, so every year he and his family returned to Hungary for an extended visit. Chad and I covered the Medical Examiner's Office while he was out of the country, which of course meant working there not only on weekends, but during the week as well. We were it. But we still had our residency duties at Southeastern, so we had to be in two places at once.

To do this, Chad taught me the "two-office trick," which enabled me to do two jobs on the same day, and no one would know:

On the days I covered the Medical Examiner's Office, I got up very early and started my work at the medical examiner's facilities at 5 a.m. Once there, I did all the work that needed to be done – autopsies, external exams, dictations, and paperwork. I finished that work about 9 or 10 a.m. Then I drove to Southeastern and I went high profile. I breezed through my fellow residents' offices, did any work that needed to be done, and was absolutely sure to go to any noon conferences, including Dr. Hollis's Thursday noon conference (*especially* Dr. Hollis's conference) but also any other noon conferences on the other days. At the conferences I made my presence known – answered questions and asked questions. Then at about 2:30 in the afternoon, I phoned the Medical Examiner's Office to see if there was any work to be done. If there was work to do, I drove back to the Medical Examiner's Office and did what needed to be done. If there was no more work to do at the Medical Examiner's office, I completed the day at Southeastern.

Because of this medical examiner's work, I was doing more autopsies. Hopefully I would be better prepared for my next autopsy rotation with Dr. Hollis.

CHAPTER 36

A three-month microbiology rotation followed my three-month blood bank rotation. During those two rotations, I did my assigned duties, but after that I wandered back to my office, or went to the library, or wherever there was peace and quiet, and I studied my butt off. I prepared for my next rotation with Dr. Hollis.

I read pathology textbooks cover to cover, many times. Of course I read and reread Dr. Hollis's textbook, but others as well – Lauren Ackerman's *Textbook of Surgical Pathology*, and Scheuer's *Liver Biopsy Interpretation*, and many others. There was a heck of a lot to learn, and the only way to learn it was rear end in chair, studying. The material wasn't necessarily that technically or scientifically challenging – I mean it wasn't like I was a mathematician/physicist working on the unified field theory, or trying to quantitate the amount of dark matter in the universe, or trying to solve a previously unsolved math equation. Some of the material involved understanding various pathophysiologic processes like healing, inflammation, neoplasia, molecular biology and the like, but learning scientific/medical concepts came relatively easy to me, and mastering this material was not necessarily that difficult. Much of what I had to learn was simply a large body of known knowledge. No one ever learned it all.

Dr. Hollis came the closest. He had a list of references, a book really, of source documents he had used to write his textbook. Having studied his textbook (and others) thoroughly, the next step was to work my way through his references, studying them one by one. As Dr. Hollis had done, I read each reference, I noted the pertinent points on an index card, and filed the cards in the same order as the chapters in his textbook. I spent most evenings this way, well into the night.

There were thousands of references typewritten single spaced and placed in three large ring binders. At the rate I was going, reading all the references would take longer than my lifetime.

Chuck Weber was the only resident who had read all the references. He was two years ahead of me, a third-year resident when I started. Like Dr. Hollis, he wrote coverage of each reference on an index card and filed it. His collection of index cards rivalled the collection of Dr. Hollis. He was smart and must have worked very fast.

Dr. Hollis, as I have made quite clear, was not a mentor to me. He was a mentor to Chuck.

Chuck patterned his life after Dr. Hollis, with differences in a few minor details. He read everything that Dr. Hollis had read, and believed everything Dr. Hollis said. Nobody was more adept at the "brain game" than Chuck; I never saw him stumped. Dr. Hollis had a small refrigerator in his office filled with Cokes, and Chuck did too, although his refrigerator was stocked with Dr. Pepper. Dr. Hollis came to work early in the morning, and Chuck showed up at the same time. Dr. Hollis wore his hair short, and so did Chuck. Every Tuesday and Thursday afternoon Dr. Hollis played touch football; Chuck was there for every game.

When Chuck finished up his residency, he joined the Southeastern faculty, helping Dr. Hollis review autopsies. Thus, during my final autopsy rotation, I presented cases to not only Dr. Hollis, but his disciple, Chuck. Chuck also helped Dr. Hollis teach pathology to the second-year medical students.

Fred Adams, one of my fellow residents, said about Chuck: "I wish he would do *something* original."

CHAPTER 37

Chuck Weber not only showed up at the Tuesday and Thursday afternoon touch football games, but I heard he excelled at them. He was not nearly as tall and athletic as Dr. Hollis, but he was reasonably quick and fast. The games were played on a grass field in a large park in the city. Dr. Hollis used orange cones to mark sidelines and end zones. He brought a spigot to tap into the sprinkler system to get drinks of water. The participants were a haphazard group of medical students, pathology residents and staff, and various nonmedical guys who liked to play touch football. There were usually about five players on a team. This was information I heard, not something I observed. I was too busy my first year or so at Southeastern just trying to survive. I had no time or energy for football.

Dr. Hollis knew I had played varsity tennis in college, and that I played matches often with Dr. Eisen (usually losing), and with Chad Sharon (usually winning), so he surmised that I liked sports and was reasonably athletic. From time to time he suggested that I come and play football with his gang.

Finally I did. Chuck and Dr. Hollis were both there; they were always there. It was a sunny chilly fall day, football weather. We were dressed in sweats and tennis shoes. Chuck was a good player, although not as good as Dr. Hollis. No one was as good as Dr. Hollis. When he went out for a pass, no one could cover the moves of this "old man" in his forties. He had been practicing for decades. He wasn't that fast – I could probably beat him in a straight forty-yard dash, but cover him one on one on a pass play – forget about it.

Chuck and I were on the same team; Dr. Hollis was on the other team. Of course, first play, I had to cover Dr. Hollis one on one. He made some cuts and moves, and I couldn't keep up. He was open by twenty yards and caught the pass for a nice gain.

Chuck said, "You saw what they did, didn't you?"

I didn't have a clue.

"They ran a crossing route."

News to me.

"Next time they do that, we'll switch, okay?"

Right.

As I write these words, fifty years later, I can't give you a play-by-play analysis of the game. I do know I made some good plays, and I made some bad plays, and I made some okay plays.

I do remember the last play of the game. It was nearing time to quit, and Dr. Hollis's team had the ball, driving, down by a touchdown. It was fourth down, near our goal line – last play. They score, game's tied. They don't score, we win. The last play was a pass from Dr. Hollis to the guy running in front of me, right to left, and the receiver I was supposed to be covering. The pass was low. I dove forward, trying to knock down the pass, which I did. Something hard hit my right chest/ribs; I found out later it was the knee of the receiver, but at the time it felt like a cricket batter whacking my right side instead of the ball. I stayed on the ground, gasping, totally unable to breathe, wind knocked out of me. As those of you who have experienced this know, it's a horrible feeling to try to breathe and not be able to – there's a medical term, "feeling of impending doom," that covers it.

Everyone stood around me, waiting for me to recover and get up. I finally did, although it was still painful to breathe and would be for a couple of weeks. I had obviously cracked a rib or two.

Dr. Hollis said, "Good God, Jack, it's just a game!"

To Dr. Hollis, it was not just a game.

CHAPTER 38

When I finished my blood banking and microbiology rotations it was late fall and early winter, and time for my three-month rotation at the Children's Hospital, doing pediatric pathology. The workload was heavy, and learning the pathology of pediatric patients was difficult. The challenge was that children are not humans, at least with respect to disease – they are a different species. Kids get different diseases and different tumors. Much of what I had learned so far during my pathology residency did not apply to children. Conditions that looked benign in kids were actually malignant, and the converse was true – things that looked malignant under the microscope were really benign.

The other challenge was the rotation duties were not confined to just autopsies or just surgical pathology or just hematology – I had to do all that stuff. I did autopsies on pediatric patients, looked at surgical pathology specimens from kids, and did clinical pathology as well. For example, I did a lot of hematology, looking at peripheral blood smears, bone marrows, and lymph nodes. It was the only rotation I had where I had to do both anatomic and clinical pathology at the same time.

It was hard, but I learned a lot. There was only one pediatric pathologist on the faculty at the time, Dr. Sprague, who was based at the Children's Hospital, and he did it all – a really smart guy. One of our patients had a rare disease, with some unusual changes in the liver, which had never been described before. Dr. Sprague and I wrote up our findings, which we eventually published in *Archives of Pathology and Laboratory Medicine*.

CHAPTER 39

For the first two years of my residency, I struggled. The only way I survived was to use the best advice I ever got, which I received right before my third year of medical school. I was really worried about that year, which was a series of rotations on surgery, internal medicine, pediatrics, and every other clinical specialty. It would last ten months, and then there would be three days of final exams covering what we were supposed to learn, from the first rotation to the last. I expressed my worries to an internal medicine resident, an acquaintance of mine, who obviously had been through it and survived. I asked him how he did it. Here is what he said.

"Each day just be sure to do the things you have to do, and then don't worry. Do what you are told – start the intravenous lines on three patients, do five histories and physicals, hold the retractor for the appendectomy, deliver the baby – do what you have to do that day, no matter how long it takes, and then don't worry. Each day there will be more things to do that it would be nice to do but are not mandatory – attend the lecture of a visiting famous academic, read the latest *Nature* article on some rare disease one of your patients has, attend a lecture on antibiotics, study for your tests at the end of the year, and many, many other things. Look, if you can do that stuff, fine. But if you don't get to it, don't worry. Don't worry that you missed the lecture, that you aren't getting any studying done, that you're not learning enough, that you are going to flunk your finals…just do what you have to do that day, and believe me, the future will take care of itself. You will pass the exams in the summer, you will learn what you need to know, you will do fine on part two of your boards; just each day do what you have to do and don't worry about the rest."

That was what I did. I survived the third year of medical school, and I did fine on my finals and had high scores on part two of the boards.

I never saw that internal medicine resident again. I don't remember his name. I believe he was sent into my life to teach me one thing, and that one thing only, and then move on.

So that was what I did during the first couple of years of my pathology residency. Each day I did what I had to do. If there was a 7 a.m. case presentation, I prepared for it and did that one thing. If there was a histology class instead, I was sure to read the chapter to be covered, do that one thing even if nothing else got done that day; things that could wait were put off. If there was a brain exam scheduled for the next morning, I not only read up on the topic to be discussed, but I reviewed neuroanatomy no matter how tired I was, or how late the hour, because I knew Dr. Hollis would test me with the brain game. Sometimes what needed to be done I did just in time; more than once I looked at my assigned dermatopathology conference slide about five minutes before the conference, which meant I was not well prepared, and it showed – but each day I got done what I had to get done that day.

Each day there were countless other things that didn't get done – work on that coagulation talk I was scheduled to deliver to the department a few months down the line; organize my autopsy paperwork, which was piling up; trim tissue; go to the educational conferences, which happened every day – each day the list of things I didn't get done was endless – but I did the things that day that I had to do that day.

That approach worked. It just took practice, about two and a half years of practice and study, almost every day, almost every waking hour – but by the end of my Children's Hospital rotation, pathology finally started to make sense. Here is a metaphor about what the process was like:

Once I had to dig a hole for a new mailbox, in front of my new house. The contractor loaned me an old-fashioned handheld post-hole digger. It had two steel blades at the bottom attached to a varnished wood handle with two prongs, one for each blade. The contraption was easy to use: simply drop or slam the blades on the ground, squeeze the blades together, and lift out the dirt – voilà, a hole. It didn't work that way. It was a dry hot July in the south, and the clay was hard, hard as a rock. In fact, there were rocks at the surface, and gravel too and concrete debris, remnants of the new road in front of the new house. I dropped the shovel on the ground and it bounced off, no progress. I did the same thing again with no result. Over and over again I dropped and slammed the post-hole digger on the hard ground, and there was no hole, not even the start of a hole. No wonder the contractor had deferred this task to me. My shoulders got tired, and I was about ready to give up. Finally, I started making some progress, only a millimeter or so to begin with, but then I gradually broke through the hard surface to reach softer ground underneath, and the progress was rapid. A few minutes later I had a hole deep enough to work. The rest happened fast. I mixed some cement, poured it into the hole, put the pole of the mailbox in the cement, waited for the cement to turn to concrete, and covered up the hole. The mailbox is still standing.

Pathology training was like that. At the start it seemed like I was not learning anything. For weeks and months, even years, it seemed like I was making no progress, as ignorant as ever.

Then, like breaking through a hard surface, pathology started to make sense; what I saw through the microscope was no longer a bewildering pattern and mixture of blue and red, but something similar to what I had seen before, that I could interpret. And the same thing occurred with other aspects of pathology – surgical specimens and autopsies didn't overwhelm me anymore. I could do this.

Another metaphor: proficiency in pathology was like a Christmas tree, which starts as a small plant, frail. Then it shoots up, eventually becoming a tree. There are branches, and one can hang ornaments on them. But the core is the trunk, with its roots.

Learning pathology was similar. I learned a little knowledge at the start, added to it, a trunk of learned concepts about inflammation, healing, neoplasia – the foundation of pathology. Then I branched out – a branch of lung pathology, liver pathology, yet another branch of neuropathology, and I hung ornaments, little pieces of knowledge on each branch – something applicable to the liver went on the liver branch, the lung pearls went on the lung branch...until I had large Christmas tree covered with tinsel and ornaments.

I suspect other professions are like that. A person goes to law school and learns a trunk of knowledge – contracts, the principle of proximate cause, and the like. Once these concepts are learned, an attorney can hang ornaments on the branches – one for wills and estate planning, one for criminal law, another for divorce law, and so on.

The trick of the thing is to stay with it.

CHAPTER 40

The calendar year came to an end, and so did my rotation at Children's Hospital; it was time for a three-month rotation with Dr. Hollis, which would be my final rotation with Dr. Hollis. It started on New Year's Day, and I noted with dismay that it was a leap year, so I would have one extra day on his rotation.

I got off to a promising start. The first case I presented was a prematurely born infant, who tragically only lived a few days after birth. The clinicians and the family requested the autopsy to learn what had happened, to hopefully give some information to the clinicians and maybe some comfort to the family. I examined the lungs and easily diagnosed hyaline membrane disease. When I finished the dissection, I went back to my office and pulled out my index cards on hyaline membrane disease. I had read all of Dr. Hollis's references on the subject.

The day I did the autopsy I had not dissected the brain because it was too soft. It was fixing in formalin. However, from my studies, I was convinced that it would show intraventricular brain hemorrhage, a common complication of patients with hyaline membrane disease. I was certain that such hemorrhage had caused the death of this unfortunate infant.

Next morning, I was totally correct. Dr. Hollis agreed with the diagnosis of hyaline membrane disease, and since I had read all his references, I was able to answer every question he put to me, including, "What was the cause of death?"

My answer was an intraventricular brain hemorrhage, even though no one, including me, had examined the brain. We finished up except for the brain. Dr. Hollis asked, "Can we look at the brain now?"

116

Fine with me.

Dr. Hollis made one incision, and right where it was supposed to be, where I predicted it would be, was the intraventricular brain hemorrhage, the cause of death. Dr. Hollis told me to be sure to take some photographs. I went to do so.

"Nice to have a good resident for a change," he said.

CHAPTER 41

My time in the good graces of Dr. Hollis did not last long. Pathology is a humbling specialty. I should have known that after Dr. Hollis said such good things about me, something would take me down.

My Waterloo involved a forty-five-year-old woman who died of pernicious anemia. Pernicious anemia is caused by vitamin B12 deficiency, or to be more accurate, a lack of "intrinsic factor" secreted by the stomach that is needed for vitamin B12 to be absorbed from the food the patient eats. It is very treatable, with vitamin B12 shots. But to render this effective treatment, pernicious anemia has to be diagnosed. Unfortunately it was not diagnosed until her last admission to the hospital. By then it was too late.

My examination revealed severe spinal cord lesions characteristic of pernicious anemia. These lesions caused neurologic symptoms so bad that toward the end of the lady's life she could not walk and had to use a wheelchair. I observed some large structures in her pulmonary arteries, which I interpreted as postmortem clots, of no significance.

The morning review was attended by a couple of other pathology residents and an internal medicine resident, Fred Lane, the clinician who finally correctly diagnosed the pernicious anemia. Fred was a good friend of Sid Steinberg, my fellow pathology resident, which made Fred a friend of mine. In fact, once Fred and I had helped plan a surprise birthday party for Sid.

That Thursday morning started out badly for me. The patient had experienced Cheyne-Stokes breathing toward the end of her life, and Dr. Hollis asked me to explain the pathophysiology of Cheyne-Stokes breathing. I couldn't do it. Cheyne-Stokes breathing describes a pattern of shallow agonal breathing at various rates – fast, then slow, and then almost stopped, then fast, slow, stopped…which repeats over and over.

I should have been able to explain how and why such breathing happened, and I couldn't, which was bad enough. But then it got worse. When called on, Fred gave a perfect, succinct, cogent explanation of Cheyne-Stokes breathing. This is a brief summary of what he said: "In Cheyne-Stokes breathing the circulation to the respiratory centers of the brain is impaired, for any number of reasons, as death approaches, so the level of oxygen and carbon dioxide can't be sensed accurately by the respiratory centers in the brain. For example, the brain thinks oxygen levels are low and carbon dioxide levels are high, so there is rapid breathing as the brain commands the body to breathe rapidly and get the levels where they are supposed to be. The resultant overreaction causes the oxygen levels in the blood to go too high and the carbon dioxide levels to go too low. The brain senses that imbalance, so commands the body to stop breathing. In summary, Cheyne-Stokes breathing is like what happens in a house with poor circulation of air, and the thermostat is in the attic, but the air conditioner and heater are in the basement. The thermostat doesn't get readings that correlate with what the temperature in the house really is, so the temperature in the house overshoots one way or the other, making the house always too hot or too cold."

But I didn't say all that. Fred did. An internal medicine resident knew pathophysiology better than I did. Dr. Hollis exclaimed with dismay, "What kind of residents are they sending me?!"

It went downhill from there. The immediate cause of death of the patient was in doubt, which was why the postmortem exam was requested, and one of the reasons Fred was there. The last organs we looked at were the lungs.

The structures I diagnosed as insignificant postmortem clots were actually antemortem clots, which had caused the patient's death. They were clots (thromboemboli) that had come from the legs, where they had formed due to the patient's inactivity (remember the patient was confined to a wheelchair) and ended up in the lungs, where they killed her. I blew it. Here's the way it happened:

Dr. Hollis placed the lungs on the cutting board, the last organs to be examined and the most significant organs. "What are the structures in the pulmonary arteries?" he asked. "All will look, and all will write."

Of course, I was already committed. I had turned in my Preliminary Anatomic Diagnoses to Dr. Hollis that morning, before the autopsy review. My diagnosis of insignificant postmortem clots was already on record. It was too late to change my mind.

I was wrong. Everyone else, including Fred, interpreted the structures as massive pulmonary emboli that caused the death of the patient. Dr. Hollis asked Fred to explain his reasoning. Fred explained the various changes in the antemortem clots, describing and pointing out the findings that led him to the correct diagnosis:

1. Little notches in the structures, made by valves in the leg veins, indicating that indeed these clots had come from the leg and traveled to the lungs, killing the patient.

2. The firm nature of the structures, characteristic of their formation while the patient was still alive.

3. Most importantly, the structures had lines of Zahn, which were signs of blood clotting *before* death.

It was quite humiliating, really. Fred Lane, an internal medicine resident (albeit one who was a genius), was teaching *pathology* to me, a pathology resident. It was Dr. Hollis's dictum backwards – instead of one of his pathology residents (me) teaching pathology and medicine to a member of the internal medicine department (Fred) – an internal medicine resident was teaching medicine and pathology to me, a member of the pathology department.

Dr. Hollis didn't say anything further. I had suffered enough. The look on his face told me how very disappointed he was in me. He wanted his residents to sparkle and scintillate, not look stupid and ignorant.

I did what I had to do the rest of the morning. Then I went home and stayed in bed the rest of the day and that night, like an injured animal.

First thing the next morning I ran into our chief resident, who said, "Boy, Dr. Hollis was in a horrible mood yesterday. He showed up at his noon conference snarling, barking, yelling, and chewing out everybody – the worst I've ever seen. Do you have any idea what caused him to be so upset? Did something happen at the morning autopsy review?"

I told him what had happened at the morning autopsy review.

The chief resident listened, said nothing, and walked away shaking his head.

In my fragile state, this encouragement was just what I needed.

CHAPTER 42

Dr. Hollis was a teacher, not a researcher. He wrote textbooks. He did not do scientific research, which was a shame. From time to time Dr. Hollis and I saw "experiments of nature," which really should have been published in the medical literature.

For example, I presented to Dr. Hollis the findings of a postmortem examination of a patient who died of hepatorenal syndrome. Nobody knows what causes hepatorenal syndrome. Empirically we do know that patients with liver failure tend to go on and develop renal failure, and we can describe this phenomenon as hepatorenal syndrome, but that's it. The mechanism by which the liver failure causes the kidney failure is unknown.

There are only two possibilities:

1. The liver failure leads to the presence of some chemical, maybe a toxin, that shuts down the kidneys. In toads, liver failure leads to a secretion of glomerulopressin, which does just that. But we're not toads. A comparable chemical cause has not been found in humans.

2. The liver failure causes the nerves to the kidneys to send signals to the kidneys that shut them down – say by causing some changes in blood flow to the extent the kidneys don't work.

That's it.

Nature presented me with an experiment that could have helped answer the question. I did an autopsy on a patient who died with hepatorenal syndrome. There was only one kidney involved in the patient's hepatorenal syndrome, a transplanted kidney, because the patient's original diseased kidneys had been removed. Again, the only kidney in the patient was a transplanted kidney.

Here's where it gets interesting: in a transplanted kidney, the nerves to the kidney have been cut – you have to cut them to get the kidney out of the donor to transplant into the recipient. Therefore, the fact that this patient developed hepatorenal syndrome with a transplanted kidney pretty much ruled out a nerve-related cause for the hepatorenal syndrome (option two above), leaving option one above as a more likely cause.

I was excited about this and thought that this finding needed to be published in the scientific/medical literature as soon as possible. I was already working on one paper with Dr. Sprague, our pediatric pathologist, and I wanted to get right to work publishing this fascinating information about hepatorenal syndrome as well. I was excited that Dr. Hollis and I could work together to write it up and get it published. This was important.

Dr. Hollis had no interest whatsoever in working on this project. "Go ahead and publish it," he said.

"Are you interested in working on it, helping me?"

"No, but you go ahead."

That was the end of it.

CHAPTER 43

Organ transplants were a new technology in the 1970s, like Silicon Valley technology is today. Kidney transplants became prevalent during my medical school and residency years. At Southeastern I did several autopsies on patients who had received renal transplants, suffered complications, and died. The autopsies were technically difficult because the anatomy was in disarray after the transplant operation. The original diseased kidneys were gone, replaced by scars in the flank regions. The transplanted kidney was put in a different location, the pelvis. This resulted in scarring there as well, so it was hard to find and dissect tissues in the region, including the ureter on its course to the urinary bladder.

Dr. Hollis did not think highly of transplant operations, which was understandable, considering the poor results we saw in the morgue. A chart of one of the deceased patients was always thick with documented problems:

1. Postoperative complications.

2. Complications as the recipient's immune system tried to reject the transplanted kidney. Preventing this normal reaction required medicines to suppress the immune system, with resultant side effects.

3. The immune system suppression prevented the body from fighting invading organisms. The resultant infections tended to be unusual, exotic, and hard to diagnose and treat.

It took time, money, and effort to treat all these complications. Dr. Hollis thought it was a waste, especially in view of the resulting poor quality of life. The patients who made it to the morgue had been in and out of hospitals frequently, and Dr. Hollis thought that was no way to live.

This opinion was probably related to selection bias. Dr. Hollis and I did not encounter the renal transplant recipients who did well, were working, paying taxes, playing golf, and having a high old time; we encountered the ones who died.

Heart and liver transplants were still extraordinary procedures in the 1970s, and I never did an autopsy on a patient who received one of those organs.

However, I did do an autopsy on a patient who received a pancreas transplant. The transplant operation had been big news, the first such transplant in the whole state and one of the earliest ones in the country. It was cutting-edge medicine. The story led off the local nightly TV news and was on the front page of the newspapers. The coverage was adulatory, filled with local pride. The Mayo Clinic and those medical centers back East had nothing on us.

The celebration lasted five days. Then, unfortunately, the patient died.

So why was the pancreas transplant done? Well, the forty-five-year-old male patient was diabetic, with high sugar levels, due to lack of insulin, which was not being secreted by his diseased pancreas. The high sugar levels were causing complications. Therefore, like many diabetic patients, he required frequent insulin shots, which were becoming problematic. A possible solution, then, was to transplant a functioning pancreas from a deceased organ donor into the recipient patient, which hopefully would secrete the needed insulin.

It worked, and the media trumpeted the resultant normal sugar levels and how well the pancreas was functioning. I paid close attention to the media coverage and thought there was too much emphasis on the pancreas and not enough on the patient.

I was not surprised, then, that five days after the operation the recipient died, and I was called upon to do an autopsy on the deceased patient. The media reported the patient's death instantly, emphasizing that according to the surgeons and the rest of the transplant team, right up to the time the patient died, the pancreas had functioned perfectly, appropriately secreting insulin, and that the patient's sugar levels had been normal ever since the transplant. Thus "the operation was a success."

Well, the pancreas may have been functioning fine, but as I did the autopsy, it was clear that nothing else was. The patient had suffered respiratory problems during and after the operation, with shock and loss of normal blood flow. This caused irreversible damage to several organs, especially the brain, which was severely damaged – swollen and even softer than the usual. Simply put, the brain was dead, which meant that the patient was dead. The rest of the autopsy revealed shock-type lesions in most of the organs.

Not being particularly susceptible to shock, the transplanted pancreas was normal.

I was glad to have the autopsy over with. However, it wasn't over. The afternoon following the autopsy, Chuck Weber, now a part of the faculty, informed me that Channel Five news would be coming at 5 p.m. for a live on-air interview about the autopsy results. Dr. Hollis was already gone for the day, and I was the only one who knew anything about the case, so it was up to me to represent the department and talk to Channel 5 news. This terrifying development was confirmed by everyone I talked to, residents and faculty alike.

I spent the rest of the afternoon reading everything I possibly could to get ready for the interview – the patient's chart, my findings, and the medical literature on diabetes. By 5 p.m. I was ready.

No one showed up – no one from Channel 5 or any other TV station. The bogus interview was a ruse. My colleagues sure could be funny sometimes.

My only comfort was that I was not the only victim of a practical joke, or the only one who fell for one. Even Dr. Hollis was not immune:

Dr. Hollis was an avid, make that *extreme* fan of the local pro football team, the Atlanta Falcons. He relished spending Sunday afternoons in the fall attending the games.

One year the team decided to change how they allocated season tickets. Dr. Hollis enlisted his several sons to get to the box office early, days early, and take turns "camping out" so that they would be near the front of the line and get great tickets.

Sure enough, Dr. Hollis procured very enviable tickets, around the forty-five-yard line, twenty rows back – perfect. Dr. Hollis bragged about these wonderful tickets a lot. Actually he bragged about them a little too much.

One of the assistants in the Pathology Department knew someone who worked in the football team offices. That person had access to the organization's stationary with official letterhead and logo. With this paperwork in hand, the pathology residents and staff composed a letter, which went something like this:

"Dear Dr. Hollis:

Because of a prior commitment, which we cannot break, we regret to inform you that we will be unable to fulfill your ticket order. We apologize. We will refund the cost of those tickets to you.

As a consolation, you may have your choice of tickets at the goal line or in the end zone, whichever you prefer, *free of charge*. Please let us know your preference. Thank you for supporting the team. Go Falcons!"

The letter was signed with the official signature of the well-known general manager of the team, and the official-looking envelope was mailed from the appropriate zip code.

Dr. Hollis believed every word, his hopes of great seats dashed. When he got the letter, he was like a scorned King Lear as he raged and complained to everyone who would listen about how horribly he had been treated. Everyone agreed with him, of course, and commiserated with him – until they were far enough away that they could burst out laughing.

After about three hours of fun, a few courageous individuals revealed the caper to him. I was not one of them.

CHAPTER 44

It was not all fun and games though. There was a dark side to the training. The culture of the department was that our pathology residency was an initiation into a brotherhood of Southeastern pathologists. We were regarded as tough, smart, young, and invincible.

Therefore, we received no training whatsoever about precautions to take around the infectious diseases like meningitis and tuberculosis that we encountered during our work with infected blood and tissues. Similarly there was no course or training about precautions to take regarding diseases spread by blood and tissue, like viral hepatitis, perhaps in part because the plague AIDS/HIV had not yet happened in the 1970s.

We used formalin/formaldehyde every day during our surgical pathology and autopsy rotations to preserve organs and prepare tissue samples for microscopic exam. It was as ubiquitous as water. Formalin is very toxic. The immediate effect of the fumes was to irritate our noses and eyes in a burning fashion. If formalin got on our skin, it burned too. Over the medium term, formalin exposure resulted in headaches and fatigue. The effects of long-term exposure to formalin are unknown, but may increase the risks of certain types of cancer. OSHA now requires monitoring of air levels of formalin, which has to be within prescribed limits, both short term and long term. During my four-year residency, no one was ever monitored for formalin. If formaldehyde bothered us, well, that was just part of it – time to man up.

Similarly, there was no training about the proper use of the tools we used – knives, scalpels, electric saws, and pincers, which had to have sharp blades to work. Thus, a person dissecting tissues could easily cut through skin; it was bad enough to get such a wound in a sterile fashion, but to get cut with a blade contaminated with blood and tissue was obviously quite hazardous and potentially lethal. We received no instructions about how to safely handle these dangerous tools and equipment. There were no safety training sessions, handouts, or meetings. Nothing.

We were on our own. I'm sure the thinking of those in authority went like this: these are trainees, but they are also physicians, graduates of medical school, so they ought to have the brains and smarts to take care of themselves. If they are not, then they are not worthy of the training Southeastern offers. Also, we, the faculty, have the same exposure to the formalin as the residents, and we use sharp objects too.

We dressed in scrubs. In addition we wore latex gloves and a plastic apron hanging around the neck and tied in the back. That was our personal protective equipment.

Twice I cut myself with a bloody scalpel blade as I dissected tissues from patients who had died of viral hepatitis, a disease transmitted by blood. Each time I hauled myself off to the emergency room, where I told what had happened to a fellow resident working in the ER, who gave me a big ole shot of gamma globulin in the butt. There was no incident report, no report to OSHA, no investigation to see if work practices could be improved, no workman's comp…nothing. No one cared.

The gamma globulin must have worked, or I have a hell of an immune system, because that was fifty years ago, and I have never had signs or symptoms of hepatitis. Every test I have ever had for evidence of viral hepatitis has been negative; my liver function tests have always been normal. I regard this outcome a true miracle.

Hepatitis was scary, but not as scary as Creutzfeldt-Jakob disease (CJD), which terrorized a fellow resident of mine during my second autopsy rotation that third year of my residency.

CJD affects only the brain with severe neurologic symptoms ending in death in less than a year, always. There is no cure. There is no treatment. It's Alzheimer's disease on steroids. The diagnosis can be made clinically, without exam of brain tissue, but this is difficult.

The cause of CJD is so strange that it sounds like science fiction, but it's true. The infectious etiologic agent of CJD is called a prion. A prion is a protein, an infectious protein, but it has neither deoxyribonucleic acid (DNA) nor ribonucleic acid (RNA), so it's not alive, it can't reproduce, it is not an organism.

And since it is not alive, it's impossible to kill. In fact, it is almost impossible to inactivate. A prion is impervious to any of the usual sterilization techniques. Measures that inactivate viruses, bacteria, parasites, fungi, and every other infectious agent do not work against the agent that causes CJD.

How the etiologic agent, the prion, infects a patient is usually unknown. However, we are certain that it can be transmitted by contaminated brain tissue. There have been at least five hundred persons who were infected with CJD in this manner.

What is really terrifying is that there are case reports of histotechnologists who have apparently contracted CJD after processing and preparing microscopic slides from the brain tissue of patients who had CJD. Think of it, coming down with the disease after minimal exposure to tissue still infectious after soaking in formalin (which kills everything) and then the chemicals used in tissue processor, including various alcohols, xylene, and heated paraffin, which are toxic in their own right.

With this background out of the way, there were three of us on the autopsy service – a fourth-year resident named Mick DePriest, one other fourth-year resident named Jeff Jones, and me. Mick was a relatively late arrival to the pathology house staff. He had done some of his training in Miami, with special interest in microbiology, doing some good research in anaerobic bacteria. He was finishing up his last two years of pathology training at Southeastern. The most striking thing about his appearance was the fact that he was only in his twenties, but had long well-combed gray hair, which he was quite proud of.

It was Saturday morning, and it was Mick's turn to take the next case – a patient who had died with suspected CJD. The clinicians wanted an autopsy to "confirm the diagnosis." The autopsy was restricted to examination of the brain only.

Mick panicked. He needed help. He knew how infectious CJD was. We all did. Because it was Saturday morning, no one in authority or anyone who knew anything was around. Dr. Hollis was on a ski trip. Dr. Page, the chairman of the department, was in San Antonio at a medical meeting. Mick was actually able to reach him, much to the dismay of Dr. Page, who just told him to "follow procedures and get it done."

Mick got it done. He and his assistant (diener) both used face shields as the skull bone was cut with the vibrating Stryker saw. Mick held a moist towel above the vibrating saw blade to cut down on exposure to bone "dust" and blood stirred up by the saw. Then he used extra care to make sure he didn't cut himself as he used a scalpel to release the brain and gently deliver it from the skull. He placed the brain in formalin, where it would remain until it firmed up enough for further examination.

When he was finished, Mick went in to a full-blown panic attack, which lasted weeks. He couldn't sleep, and he couldn't eat. He lost weight. He was slim to begin with, but with his loss of appetite, he became cachectic. He couldn't work, so Jeff and I took him off the service, and the two of us took turns doing all the autopsies. Mick aged perceptibly. His hair turned even grayer, almost white.

He panicked for these reasons:

1. No one knows exactly how CJD is transmitted, so it was impossible to rule out some significant exposure during the brain removal.

2. No blood test exists to determine whether someone has CJD. The only way to make the diagnosis is a brain tissue exam. So Mick could not do follow-up lab tests on himself to see whether or not he had CJD, or was going to develop CJD.

3. The incubation period for CJD is long, years to decades. Thus for Mick, there was no time period when he could be certain he wasn't going to get this incurable disease, not a month, not a year, not a decade, maybe not a lifetime.

Mick's big hope was that the CJD diagnosis was not certain (that was why the autopsy was done), and therefore there was a chance the microscopic slides would demonstrate some other disease, with no risks to Mick. "I am so hoping the slides show something other than CJD," Mick told me.

Not to be. The slides showed classic CJD, so Mick continued his panic attack.

After three weeks Mick recovered enough to come back to work and resume normal life. We put him back on the autopsy rotation.

Mick said, though, that he would never be the same, and that this event had changed his life. "Jack," he said, "I was shocked there was *no one* who could or would help me – not Dr. Hollis, not the chairman of our department, not our neuropathologist…no one. I was on my own. No one will take care of me, and until this happened, I never realized that."

Mick never did come down with Creutzfeldt-Jakob disease. I ran into him about thirty years later at a hematopathology meeting. He was in good health and really hadn't aged that much.

Mick did not come down with CJD, and I never got hepatitis. Actually, to my knowledge, none of the pathology residents ever had any work-related illnesses or maladies.

This was a miracle. Keep in mind, that as we did our work in the autopsy suite, any infectious agent we encountered…had won.

CHAPTER 45

So why did we pathology residents put up with it? Simple, we wanted to be pathologists. That's all we wanted to be, and the only way to achieve that end was to go through the Southeastern residency program or some program like it. And we thought, rightly or wrongly, that Southeastern was the best pathology program for us, because of Dr. Hollis. And the reward at the end of the process was that we would help patients and make a good living. I don't want to get too maudlin here, but we thought our cause was noble.

Also, I hope I have made this clear, pathology was fun. It was interesting to study the human body because it is such a marvel of engineering and beauty, even if what we were studying was what had gone awry. We pathologists were like mechanics working on a Ferrari. I could see, touch, feel, even smell what was wrong with the patient: the diseased appendix of acute appendicitis was right in front of me where I could see the hemorrhage, congestion and pus; touch and feel the resultant swelling; if the appendicitis was severe with gangrene, I could smell that. The next day I could look at the slides of the acute appendicitis under the microscope and be transported to another world, the microscopic realm, as I looked at the tissues under 40X, 100X, and 400X magnification. I could see the white blood cells infiltrating the appendix like an invading army, and the congestion – the prominent blood vessels gorged with blood like a mountain stream when the dam is released.

Therefore, to me, and the rest of my resident colleagues, becoming a pathologist was more than important to us; it was our life. In that sense we were lucky. For us a pathology residency was a dream come true. What a gift! How many people get to follow their dream? We were in our mid-twenties and we knew exactly what we wanted to do; we had purpose in our lives. Many our age at the time didn't know what they wanted to do. Some still don't.

Dr. Woolridge, my pathology teacher in medical school, once said that there are two main problems in the world:

1. Overpopulation.

2. Too many people do not have a purpose in their lives.

That's debatable. If he's right, I couldn't do much single-handedly about overpopulation, but I sure had a purpose in my life – to be a good pathologist.

My fellow pathology residents had the same philosophy, so there was a lot of comradery, even away from work. Sometimes one of the residents would host a party – grill hamburgers and then play games. A couple of times all of us went to a park, where we had a picnic and then played softball and touch football. Dr. Sprague, the Children's Hospital pathologist, once hosted a swimming party for the residents and their families.

Sarah and I lived a frugal life. A big night out was dinner at a Mexican restaurant, which we could afford because the food was cheap, tasty, and filling. A purchase of a record album was a big dent to our budget. I drove a Dodge Colt, cheapest car I could find, but reliable. Car expenses or dental expenses were a real setback. One of the reasons I moonlighted at the Medical Examiner's Office was to have enough money for us to survive. Sarah, my wife, worked as an administrative assistant for a medical supply company until the birth of our first son during my second year of residency. Then she became a stay-at-home mom.

I didn't see them much. I noticed that if I missed seeing my son for a day or two, I had missed something important, because in the time span of that one day he had changed – because he changed every day.

Nothing was more important to me than being a good physician/pathologist – more important than wife, family, sleep, recreation, health…everything.

I have a picture taken of me during my last year at Southeastern, for an identification badge. Picture IDs, other than driver's licenses, were a new concept at the time. In that picture I am obviously trying to mirror Dr. Hollis. When Sarah saw the picture, she didn't like it at all and said, "You could have at least smiled." When my parents saw it, they said, "That's not a good picture of you."

That was who I was at the time.

CHAPTER 46

One year, on a day in early October, a researcher at Vanderbilt Medical School, Dr. Earl Sutherland, won the Nobel Prize in medicine for his work on cyclic adenosine monophosphate (AMP), which uses an enzyme to produce adenosine triphosphate (ATP – pronounced A Tee Pee). This hurt, because we regarded Vanderbilt as a rival for best medical school in the Southeast. We wished a researcher at Southeastern had won.

Not to be outdone, one day Dr. Hollis prefaced a lecture by saying although he had not won the Nobel Prize, he did know something about biochemistry. He proceeded to draw a Native American tent (i.e., tepee) on the blackboard, turned to the class, and said, "This is ATP."

CHAPTER 47

I never learned much about Dr. Hollis's personal life. One day I was looking at some slides with Dr. Hollis in his office when he received a phone call from his wife, Ellen Hollis. A discussion ensued about a refrigerator breakdown and what to do – repair it, buy a new refrigerator, and if to buy one, what kind?

"Well, I guess we'll just have to go with that one," Dr. Hollis concluded.

Along with most of the pathology residents, I attended the wedding of one of his daughters. Dr. Hollis and his wife had a lot of kids, hard to tell how many, maybe seven or eight. I met Ellen Hollis, a vivacious attractive brunette, who didn't put up with any crap from Dr. Hollis. During the evening festivities when there was some setback that upset Dr. Hollis, I overheard her whisper, "Drop it, Darrell" – and he did.

CHAPTER 48

I finished my last autopsy rotation with Dr. Hollis on March 31. For six months I had worked every day, literally. Of course there were no days off Monday through Friday. In addition I had worked every day of every weekend, either at Children's Hospital, the Medical Examiner's office, or at Southeastern. Some days I worked two places the same day. Luckily autopsies were not a stat procedure

That first Saturday I didn't have to work was a luxurious day. I slept late and that afternoon watched the Final Four games of the NCAA basketball tournament.

CHAPTER 49

I was young and a dreamer. I dreamt that maybe someday I would be famous and have my picture on the cover of *Time* magazine. Maybe I would go into politics; I could start out as a medical examiner in a community, a political job if there ever was one, then run for public office, become mayor, governor, senator, and who knew, maybe I would be president someday. At the time that didn't seem so farfetched; our president at the time was Jimmy Carter, who started out as a local peanut farmer in Georgia – if he could do it, I could do it. Or I dreamed of starting a little pathology company, which could grow into a big pathology company, and be rich.

I don't think our teachers, like Dr. Hollis and Dr. Page, were in it for the money. Dr. Page lived near me, and I lived in an apartment complex where those of modest means like me could afford the rent. Dr. Page lived in a one-story ranch house, not particularly fancy, a couple of blocks away in a subdivision that was certainly upper middle class, but not the kind of place a plutocrat would live. From time to time I drove by Dr. Page's home and saw him mowing his lawn on his riding lawn mower, wearing a cowboy hat.

Dr. Hollis lived in the same subdivision, again not that far from the likes of me, in a nice house but not a mansion.

CHAPTER 50

I finished my third year of residency with a three-month rotation covering two areas:

1. Dermatopathology studying skin pathology with Dr. Reed, our dermatopathologist.
2. Liver and kidney specimens with Dr. Eisen.

It was an easy Monday-through-Friday 8-to-5 kind of job. I played a lot of tennis with Dr. Eisen, who was an excellent player and almost always beat me. During the four years I was at Southeastern, I won one set.

Toward the end of my third year of residency, Dr. Page, the chairman of the department, called me in for a conference. He told me that he knew that I was moonlighting at the Medical Examiner's Office along with Chad Sharon (of course he knew!). He said that I had his approval to continue working there during the rest of my residency, but that I was not to recruit anyone to take Chad Sharon's place, who was almost finished with his residency. "It's okay for you to work there, but I don't want any of my other residents working there. You are the last one."

So ended a long tradition of Southeastern pathology residents covering the Medical Examiner's Office. I thought the attitude of Dr. Page was very misguided: I learned so much from my medical examiner's job – knowledge and experience that I could not get at Southeastern.

I didn't share these thoughts with Dr. Page. Instead, I recruited and trained a pathology resident from Emory to take Chad's place and alternate with me, covering every other weekend and the vacations taken by Dr. Musial. It was a tragedy, in my opinion, that Southeastern lost this great resource for Southeastern pathology residents to Emory, which was happy to have *its* residents moonlight at the Medical Examiner's Office. Wait a minute – Southeastern didn't lose this opportunity, but *gave it away.*

Years later, after Dr. Page retired, I ended up working in Dallas with a woman who had been a Southeastern professor in the blood bank when I was there. We sometimes reminisced about Southeastern, and I told her I was mystified: Why, if Dr. Page was so much against his residents working at the Medical Examiner's Office, did he let me do it?

She said, "That's what made Dr. Page such a great department chairman. He treated everyone in the department differently. He knew you were conscientious and that you proved you could do both jobs – be a good resident and work at the Medical Examiner's Office. He didn't think the other residents could do that, so he stopped them. Dr. Page did not treat everyone the same. He brought out the best in everyone."

CHAPTER 51

The three residents I started with when I was an intern entered the fourth and last year of pathology residency with me – Layne Siler, Fred Adams, and Sid Steinberg. Dr. Page chose Layne to be chief resident. I wanted to be chief resident, but I knew that wasn't going to happen. I mean, who was going to lobby for me to have the job? It wasn't like I **had** a mentor or anything.

CHAPTER 52

I had an easy fourth year. My rotations were all in clinical pathology, with no autopsies, no calls to come in and do rapid surgical pathology consults, in fact no on-call duties whatsoever. The rotations were 8-to-5, Monday-through-Friday jobs.

During my vacation time, I did two locum tenens jobs, one for two weeks, and one for one week. During those times a pathologist in private practice took a vacation, and I covered his practice while he was gone. I did everything – clinical pathology, surgical pathology, autopsies…without any supervision. It was great experience.

I'm sure Dr. Page would have disapproved. However, since I did this work during my vacation time, I figured it was okay. And I kept it secret. What he didn't know wouldn't hurt me.

I'm sure he knew.

CHAPTER 53

During my last year of residency, I still saw a lot of Dr. Hollis. I attended his weekly Thursday noon slide conferences. He also started a new conference every Tuesday at noon. It was a journal club. He put out medical/scientific articles for us to review, and then we showed up for his conference ready to discuss them.

They were great conferences. Dr. Hollis asked questions no one else asked, and then used the conferences and the journal articles to answer them:

1. Question: Why does your nose start running when you jog?

    Answer: Jogging makes a runner breathe hard, which brings moist hot air into contact with the relatively cool areas of the nose, so the excess moisture condensates around the nose.

2. Why do athletes – football players, basketball players – have to stretch and "loosen up" before competing?

    Answer: When a joint is not being used, the joint fluid (synovial fluid) leaves the joint space and is absorbed into the cartilage adjacent to the joint space, and stays there. The synovial fluid in the cartilage is not available to lubricate the joint, so it has to be coaxed out. Gentle loosening-up exercises get fluid from the cartilage into the joint space, like an oil can squirting lubricant onto a bicycle chain, so nothing creaks or squeaks.

CHAPTER 54

It was surprising that Dr. Hollis's dictum was "you can't not know," with its poor grammar, because Dr. Hollis demanded proper use of the English language. Any resident who said "the data shows" would be swiftly corrected by Dr. Hollis saying, "The data *show*. Data is plural; datum is singular." Dr. Hollis deplored the perceptible decline in written and verbal standards, which was happening all around him. He resolved to partially rectify the situation, at least with respect to his residents.

Therefore, for one of his Thursday noon conferences, instead of putting out microscopic slides for review, Dr. Hollis put out a photograph of a liver, with obvious pathologic changes. The assignment for the conference was to write a description of the liver, and Dr. Hollis would critique each submission for its "literary content" rather than whether the diagnosis was right or wrong. In an uncharacteristic show of mercy by Dr. Hollis, these written descriptions would not be signed, but each one would be assigned a number by Dr. Hollis's assistant, so the author would remain anonymous.

At the conference, Dr. Hollis found plenty to criticize and pointed out the many deficiencies of each of the numbered descriptions. That is, he went over each of the descriptions except for number seven, which went something like this:

"The data in this here picture, both literally and figuratively, appears to kind of want to show that this here patient may have had a mild cirrhosis of the liver, To really know that this may be the tentative findings the Doctor would has to really potentially want to knows what the patient has been exposed probably to. Like, the liver size is really large: with stuff that appears to have worn the liver out. It is a really bad looking liver..."

Dr. Hollis finished the conference having skipped number seven. The residents asked, "What about number seven?"

Dr. Hollis at first refused, saying number seven was so bad that he was afraid he would lose control, that he simply could not understand how someone in his program could and would write such an execrable description, especially after knowing what was expected. The residents persisted, "How else can we learn if you won't point out the mistakes?"

Dr. Hollis relented and began pointing out the errors in a reasonable tone: the disagreements between subject and verb, the redundancies, the ambiguous tentative statements, punctuation errors…but his voice got louder and louder as he became angrier and angrier as he pointed out error after error, shouting, "And just look at this infinitive! It hasn't just been split, it's been drawn and quartered!"

Of course, number seven had been written by a team of residents, to elicit just such a tempestuous response.

CHAPTER 55

I continued to teach the laboratory sessions of the pathology course, along with a member of the faculty. Our job was to tutor the students. We started out the session with a short lecture. Most commonly this lecture consisted of one of us using a projecting microscope to send magnified images of the slides to the screen, where we pointed out the pertinent features. Then the students could ask us questions about the slides, or whatever the lecture covered that day. When the lecture was over, the students looked at the slides at their own pace and worked independently. The faculty member and I stuck around and roamed up and down the rows of students looking through their microscopes, and answered any questions they had.

The degree of teaching talent and dedication by the pathology faculty members varied markedly. Their interests and abilities with respect to teaching were on a spectrum. At one end were those professors who were conscientious. They showed up to the lab sessions on time, prepared, did their share of the lecturing and teaching, and stayed around to answer questions.

At the other end of the spectrum were those faculty members who showed up late, or did not show up at all, were unprepared, and did little or no real teaching. The reasons for this dereliction of duties varied. Some were absentminded and just couldn't remember to show up. Others were more interested in research, and winning a Nobel Prize, or at least competing for a Nobel Prize, and just didn't care about teaching – thought it was a waste of their precious time and talents. Obviously, if a resident was paired with such a faculty member, the resident would have to do all or most of the work.

There was a similar range of teaching quality among the residents as well. Some took their teaching responsibilities seriously, and others sloughed them off, thinking they had more important things to do. If a faculty member was paired with a resident who pretty much didn't do any teaching, it would be extra work for the faculty member, who would have to do everything.

I perceived myself as one of the better residents when it came to teaching. I thought it was important to teach the craft of medicine and pathology.

However, being the lazy person I am, I always wanted to be paired with a faculty member who was a good teacher, conscientious, and who showed up on time prepared to teach and help do the work.

Never happened.

Without exception, I was always paired with a suboptimal or worthless faculty member when it came to teaching, someone who maybe was a brilliant researcher but didn't know much about general pathology, or someone who was absentminded, brilliant at abstract thought, but clueless about pragmatic matters like when it was time to show up and teach. The following conversation happened a lot:

Me: Why weren't you there to teach the lab?

Absent professor: I forgot about it.

Every year I hoped my luck would change, and I would be matched with a faculty member who was a good teacher, but I always ended up with a loser.

Of course, it wasn't bad luck. After I finished my final stint of teaching, I had a conversation with Chuck Weber, Dr. Hollis's disciple, who was no longer a resident but now on the faculty, assisting Dr. Hollis in many things, including teaching the pathology course to students. Chuck related to me that it was no secret who were the good teachers and who were the bad teachers among the faculty and residents. So each year when it came time to assign a faculty member and a house staff member to each lab section, Dr. Hollis made sure that each section had at least one good teacher, i.e., if the faculty member was a poor teacher, he was paired with a resident who was a good teacher, and vice versa. Since I was a good teacher, I was always paired with a faculty member who was a poor teacher, so that the good teachers from the faculty would be available to be paired with the residents who were poor teachers.

My fourth and last year of residency, Dr. Hollis asked me to teach the hematology part of his histology course to the first-year residents, because he wasn't that interested in that subject and preferred that I teach it. I was honored to do so.

Every month during my last year, the fourth-year residents had lunch at the faculty club, guests of Dr. Page, the Pathology Department chairman. These were not pleasant events. At each lunch I was worried that I would say or do something that would alienate him and pretty much torpedo my career in pathology.

Fortunately, that never happened.

At one lunch Dr. Page went out of his way to compliment me. Like all the residents, I had been asked to submit questions for the pathology tests administered to the second-year medical students. Dr. Page singled me out to say that the questions I had submitted were really good, and several of them had been used.

That might not sound like much, but during the whole year I was the only resident to be singled out for any kind of compliment whatsoever.

CHAPTER 56

During my last year, I looked for a job, which was challenging because pathology jobs were hard to find. There was a glut of pathologists.

I wasn't too worried though, because I was well known to the private practice group that had the contract to do the medical examiner's work where I worked for Dr. Musial. Ever since I was a third-year resident, they made it known that they very much wanted me to join their group when I finished my residency. I was flattered, of course. The downside of the potential job was that I really did not want to do a whole lot of medical examiner's work – a little would be okay, but I didn't want to be their forensic pathology guy, spending a lot of time doing medical examiner's work.

For every other pathology position I sought, there were about a hundred applicants.

Dr. Hollis helped me some with my job search. He gave me advice and was certainly willing to let me use him as a reference, and he wrote letters of recommendation for me as needed. However, he couldn't do a whole lot to help me or any of my fellow residents seeking a pathology position. There just weren't many jobs out there, for anybody.

Dr. Hollis didn't have much regard for contracts, because he thought "there's always a way to get out of them. Whether or not you trust the persons you're going to work for is what counts."

He used himself as an example:

"Jack, I have tenure at Southeastern Medical School, which means I have a contract that says I can't be fired. But I know Southeastern's lawyers could get out of it and fire me if they wanted to. Or they could just stop paying me and dare me to sue. Southeastern can pay their lawyers a lot longer than I can pay mine. Hell, they don't even have to fire me. They can just make my life miserable – say I can't teach, can't use my textbook, can't do autopsies, or can't be in charge of the residency program. They can make me leave in spite of what my contract says."

CHAPTER 57

When I started at Southeastern, three of the older residents were in the Berry Plan. The Berry Plan was a Vietnam-era program that enabled physicians in training to avoid the draft while in medical school and residency – deferring that obligation until they completed their training. Only then would they finally join the military. The three residents I knew in the Berry Plan joined the army. By the time they finished their residency, they were qualified physicians/pathologists and could get valuable medical experience in the military. The army for its part got trained physicians/pathologists. It was a win-win deal.

Except, the pathologists ended up hating their time in the army. One such individual was John Henderson, who was a fourth-year resident when I was an intern. When he finished his residency, he joined the army to fulfill his Berry Plan obligation. He was stationed at Fort Hood, located near Killeen, Texas. He didn't like Killeen and he hated the army.

We talked about it – John, Dr. Hollis, and I. The setting was the Southeastern Pathology spring banquet at the members-only Piedmont Club, the best restaurant in town, located in the top floor of a downtown skyscraper. Every spring, Dr. Page staged this event. All the present house staff and all the previous house staff were invited, as well as present and past faculty. The agenda was a drink or two, followed by a three-course meal with the best food I ever ate. Then Dr. Page would make a few remarks, extolling the virtues of the Southeastern Pathology Department. The banquet concluded when each of the fourth-year residents finishing up their training were introduced. Dr. Page gave each "graduate" a fashionable black wooden chair with a gold-colored metal plaque on the back saying *Aude Esse Verus*. I never took Latin in school, but it has been translated to me two ways "Dare to speak the truth" or "Dare to be true." I still have my chair.

Dr. Hollis, John, and I were seated together, enjoying our meal. We were seated near the window and could gaze down on the city at night from the highest point of the highest building. John was on leave for a few days, from Fort Hood, so he could attend the banquet. The conversation turned to military service, and John said he hated being in the army.

Dr. Hollis, who had served in the army himself, asked, "Why do you hate the army so much?"

"Because of the waste. The microscopic slides I get are of horrible quality; I can barely interpret them. This one day I had a lymph node specimen, and I knew that when I got the slides the next day, it would be either a malignant lymphoma or a reactive process, and it would be a difficult decision, so I would need high-quality slides. I begged the histotechs to give special attention to the case and to please, just this once, give me good slides. I prayed for good slides. But the next day the slides were as horrible as always. Nobody cared, and that's why I hate the army. The waste."

Dr. Hollis replied, "But there are a lot of wasteful things in life – waste in other things besides the military. What is it in particular about waste in the army that bothers you so?"

John couldn't answer, just shrugged and shook his head.

"I think what bothers you is this: you feel your country is not getting its money's worth. Look, I went into the army, and I was idealistic, patriotic, and willing to serve my country. I wanted to do my best, I suspect you do too, but you can't, and *that's* what bothers you."

We were all quiet.

Dr. Hollis continued, "I met physicians in the service who hated it, but wanted to serve their twenty years and then retire early, with a pension generous enough to never have to work again. I still meet physicians who are planning to do that and stick it out, even though they hate it."

The rest of us at the table nodded. We all knew people doing that – the trade-off was twenty years of your life for a big-time payoff of a long comfortable retirement.

"Not a fair trade," said Dr. Hollis. "Is there anything more valuable than time?"

CHAPTER 58

When I was looking for a job, there were essentially two career paths for someone finishing their residency:

1. Go into academic medicine. The upside was fame. A faculty member could write a textbook and be a published author, or do published research and be quoted in those textbooks or by other physicians. A famous academic pathologist got to travel to all kinds of wonderful places and give lectures or serve on various committees to advance the causes of medicine and knowledge. Also, at an academic medical center, the pathologist could practice up-to-date high-quality medicine. The downside was the low pay. The joke goes:

   Question: Why are the fights in academia so fierce?

   Answer: The stakes are so small.

2. Go into private practice. The upside was that there was potentially good money to be made in private practice, which rewarded service and productivity, not research. The downside was that the work was hard, and you toiled in obscurity.

My first choice for a job was to be on the faculty at the medical school I had attended, Ivory Medical School in Dallas, Texas, where my wife was from. Of course I knew the members of the Ivory Pathology Department, and I was able to get an interview for a job. I was not offered the job. They must have thought I was not ready, because they recommended I do another year of training, maybe in forensic pathology.

That wasn't going to happen.

CHAPTER 59

The three other residents who started with me as interns finished with me as fourth-year residents, looking for jobs just like me. My opinion at the time was that they all ended up in suboptimal situations:

Layne Siler stayed on at Southeastern to study pulmonary pathology, a fellowship.

Fred Adams also stayed at Southeastern, doing pathology at the Veterans Administration Hospital, part of Southeastern. As he described the job, it sounded to me like a fellowship.

Even Sid Steinberg, the smartest of us all, stayed at Southeastern as a surgical pathology fellow.

In each case, the pay sucked, and I thought the job kind of sucked. I regarded their jobs as essentially a fifth year of residency – more responsibility, maybe, but still under the supervision of others.

I had no interest whatsoever in staying at Southeastern, as a fellow, junior faculty, or anything that involved more training. I was impatient to be a real doctor, a real pathologist, making decisions on my own and getting good pay for doing that. I wanted a real job.

I found a real job, although it was not in Texas, where I really wanted to live, where my wife was from. I was unable to do that, because the only pathology job available was the Ivory Medical School job, which I did not get. There were literally no other pathology job openings in Texas – none.

I did get a pathology position in Meridian, Mississippi. It was a private practice job in a multispecialty group serving one hospital, with one other pathologist, who would be my partner – perfect. In fact, I already knew the pathologist I would be working with. I knew her from her days when she was on the pathology house staff at Ivory Medical Center. She had trained in pathology during the same time I was a medical student. I had high regard for her. I thought she was nice and smart. Most importantly, following Dr. Hollis's guidance, I trusted her. I signed the contract, and everything worked out.

CHAPTER 60

After a few months in private practice, I returned to Southeastern for a few days to study for my board exams.

Becoming a practicing physician was a long journey, and the final step was for me to take my "boards." If I passed these tests, I would be board certified by the American Board of Pathology in anatomic pathology and clinical pathology. To be "board certified" in my medical specialty was pretty much a requirement to actually get to practice pathology. No one wanted a pathologist who "flunked their boards." I think passing the boards for physicians is comparable to passing the bar exam for attorneys.

I returned to Southeastern to review some clinical pathology subjects. The microbiology department had a teaching set of Kodachrome slides with an accompanying study guide, which I needed to review. I also needed to get up to speed on immunofluorescence studies, something we did not do at my hospital. At the time I had to do all this "hands on," so I had to be on-site, at the Southeastern campus. I took a few days off from my job and drove to Southeastern.

Yes, I had to literally drive to Southeastern, stay at Sid Steinberg's house while I was there, get the Kodachrome slides from the microbiology department, borrow the projector in Chuck Weber's office when he wasn't using it, and go to the immunofluorescence laboratory.

Of course, now if I asked for help of this nature, I would be told "just go to our website" or "I'll e-mail you the PowerPoint." Websites and PowerPoints did not exist in the 1970s. Neither did the internet. What I would do now would have been regarded as science fiction when I reviewed for my boards; to a time traveler from contemporary times, I would have said, "You mean I can just press a key and see all this stuff on a computer screen?"

"Well, you have to use a mouse."

"A mouse. How do you tame it?"

"Never mind."

I also brought a tough case I needed help on. I needed Dr. Hollis.

The specimen was bone marrow. I had collected the specimen myself, sticking a needle in the right posterior superior iliac crest and drawing out some bone marrow, and using another needle to obtain a biopsy.

That was the easy part. The hard part was figuring out what in the heck was wrong with the patient.

This wasn't just any patient. He was an eighty-five-year-old man, a retired physician, a general practitioner, the kind who made house calls with a stethoscope around his neck, and carried a black bag filled with needles, syringes, and penicillin. He was a prominent member of the community I was now a part of. I really needed to make a diagnosis on this specimen, a *correct* diagnosis.

The patient had presented with weakness. The cause of the weakness was pretty obvious, low numbers of red blood cells, i.e., he was anemic. He not only had low red blood cells, but low platelets, so his blood couldn't clot, and low white blood cells, so his body could not fight off infections. The medical jargon for low red blood cells, low white blood cells, and low platelets – low everything, really – is to call it pancytopenia. The bone marrow produces the red blood cells, platelets, and white blood cells – so it was a good place to look to make a diagnosis.

I looked at the bone marrow, but I could not come up with a diagnosis. I just didn't know what was going on with this patient.

Since I was coming to Southeastern anyway to review for my board exams, I brought the microscopic slides of the bone marrow to go over with Dr. Hollis. Maybe he could help.

It was like old times. I sat across from Dr. Hollis at the double-headed microscope. Dr. Hollis adjusted the magnifying objectives from 4X to 10X, to 40X, and then 100X. The eyepieces had a magnification of 10X, so the final total magnification was 1000 times larger than normal.

Not surprisingly, the patient's bone marrow was shot to hell. Usually the bone marrow is a potpourri of red blood cell precursors, white blood cell precursors, and platelet precursors (called megakaryocytes), which mature in an organized fashion into functional red blood cells, white blood cells, and platelets, which are released into the blood.

But this patient's bone marrow was not like that at all. It was replaced by a haphazard collection of bizarre-appearing cells of varying sizes and shapes, which to me were not diagnostic of anything.

Dr. Hollis carefully examined each slide, moving it across the stage of the microscope side to side and up and down. He continued this laborious process until every slide was examined. Then he pushed his chair back from the microscope and rubbed the top of his head with his right hand.

Dr. Hollis said, "So, in summary, we have an elderly gentleman with pancytopenia for unknown reasons. He's not on any drugs that would wipe out his bone marrow?"

"Right," I said.

"He hasn't been exposed to any radiation?"

"Right."

"No chemotherapy?"

"Correct."

"Is he a farmer? Maybe he got exposed to pesticides, which could have done something like this to the bone marrow?"

"No, he's a physician, general practitioner, lives and works in town not in the country."

Dr. Hollis finished rubbing his head, slid his chair over to his file cabinet, sorted through his index cards, and pulled out a few.

"Here is what your patient has," he said as he handed the index cards to me. "Preleukemia, or as it's also known, myelodysplastic syndrome."

I had never heard of it.

"It's only recently been described," said Dr. Hollis. "A certain number of these patients go on to develop acute leukemia. My guess is that is that this condition happens not all that infrequently but isn't noticed until the patient has already developed full-blown leukemia. Also, since this condition usually happens in older patients, they tend to go on and die of something else before the preleukemia is diagnosed. There's not much available in the way of treatment: red blood cell transfusions for the anemia, platelet transfusions to stop any bleeding, and antibiotics for any infections that develop. That's about it."

I want this book to be a historical document. The diagnosis of myelodysplastic syndrome is commonly made in present-day medicine, so often that it has an abbreviation (MDS) well known to pathologists and oncologists. Since that day in Dr. Hollis's office, I have made the diagnosis of MDS, hundreds if not thousands of times. But in the 1970s it was a new disease, or a newly discerned disease, and the first time I diagnosed it was thanks to Dr. Hollis.

Dr. Hollis made me look good. The patient ended up going to the Mayo Clinic for treatment. The Mayo Clinic examined the bone marrow specimen. The Mayo Clinic told the patient that Dr. Spenser knew what he was doing because the diagnosis and interpretations were correct – they wouldn't change a thing.

CHAPTER 61

The three days of my board exam were in Miami, Florida, three of the most unpleasant days of my life. I was trying to get board certified in both anatomic pathology (surgical pathology and autopsy pathology) and clinical pathology (microbiology, hematology, chemistry, and blood banking). The first day and a half I was tested in anatomic pathology. The last day and a half I was tested in clinical pathology. The written exams covered the theoretical and practical aspects of pathology, with the objective being to be sure a board-certified pathologist is competent. The rooms where we took the tests were large and cold. My understanding was that in a typical year, half the test takers flunked. No one who had done their pathology training at Southeastern had ever flunked. I sure didn't want to be the first.

I was quite confident I passed the anatomic pathology part of the exam. In fact, I didn't see how I could have possibly missed a single question. Dr. Hollis had prepared me well. Layne Siler and Fred Adams, two of my fellow residents from Southeastern, were taking the test with me, and they also thought the anatomic part of the exam was easy and straightforward.

The candidates from other institutions had a different take. I overheard several talking to each other, and they were distraught about how hard the test was. "I studied tumors, and there were no questions about tumors, only pathophysiology!" was a typical comment.

I guess that was why 50% failed.

I thought the clinical pathology part of the exam was really challenging. I thought I had probably passed, but it was no sure thing.

A month later I found out I had passed both the anatomic and clinical pathology boards. I received this good news via a phone call from Dr. Page before I got written notice from the board. Dr. Page told me that I had passed, that my scores were very high, and that he was proud of me. Back then, the test takers were not informed of exact scores on any of the exams, just whether they passed or failed. Fine with me. I just wanted to be board certified, and I was. I regarded this as the final step in my training. I was through. I made it.

Chapter 62

A few months after my exams, I made another trip to Southeastern to use their photomicrograph facilities. The object of the trip was to photograph the microscopic changes of a very rare tumor of the gallbladder, which I would go on to describe and publish in the medical literature. The photomicrographic facilities I had in private practice did not deliver the high-quality photographs I needed to send to a medical journal. So again I made the several-hour trip to Southeastern, to use the same equipment Dr. Sprague and I had used to publish our case from Children's Hospital.

While at Southeastern, I stopped in to see Dr. Hollis. He was happy to see me. I brought a couple of interesting cases for him to look at.

One was a relatively rare tumor of the testis, called a stromal cell tumor, which was infrequent enough that it only makes up about 5% of testis tumors, and only one hundred cases existed in the medical literature. Dr. Hollis was not particularly interested in it. When it came to tumors, Dr. Hollis was a "lumper" rather than a "splitter." Pathologists tend to be in one camp or the other:

1. "Splitters" try to parse out each possible variant of an organ's tumors, and give each particular variant a name and its own place in the pantheon of cancers, with its own appearance, clinical behavior, prognosis, and even treatment.

2. "Lumpers" take the position that tumors, especially malignant tumors, by definition vary from normal tissue, in unpredictable ways, and that one can go crazy parsing out

each tumor variation into elaborate classification schemes. Lumpers, then, prefer to think of tumors in broad categories, with individual variations within those categories.

So Dr. Hollis, a "lumper," wasn't particularly interested in the relatively uncommon testis tumor I showed him.

However, he was thrilled with the other specimen I brought. It was simply an abdominal scar at the site of a previous surgical incision. The interesting part was that the surgeon had noticed a quite impressive mass that had developed there, which he removed and sent to me, hoping I could tell him what it was.

To me it was an obvious case of heterotopic bone (i.e., normal bone where it was not supposed to be – in this case skin and soft tissue at the site of the abdominal scar). What had happened was that cells used in healing the body and making scar tissue had changed into cells that make bone. This process was caused by inflammation related to the previous abdominal operation. Dr. Hollis had taught me such things. Dr. Hollis asked if he could keep the slides and put them out for his Thursday noon conference. Of course that was fine with me. I asked him why he was so interested in this case, simply a scar with bone in it, and he answered, "Most pathologists don't take sections of scars."

CHAPTER 63

During the next couple of years, I kept in touch with Dr. Hollis. Whenever I had an interesting specimen that might be of teaching value, I mailed slides of the case to Dr. Hollis, who used them for his Thursday noon conferences or for teaching medical students. Whenever I did so, Dr. Hollis phoned me with his thoughts on the cases and brought me up to date on the latest happenings at Southeastern.

One by one, the people I knew at Southeastern went other places. Layne Siler went into private practice at an Atlanta hospital. Fred Adams went into private practice in Rome, Georgia. Sid Steinberg went into private practice in Cincinnati, Ohio.

Of all the residents I trained with at Southeastern, not a single one ever went into academic medicine as a career. Every single one ended up in private practice, like me. Even Chuck Weber eventually went into private practice.

I have published seven medical/scientific papers. Three of them described findings I discovered at postmortem exams. The rest pertain to cytopathology, transfusion medicine, or other areas. I am proud of all of them, which have expanded medical knowledge slightly (very slightly), but perhaps significantly. In a couple of instances I discovered new medical facts, so I was the first to know what no one else knew. These facts were of negligible significance, but to be first to know and describe a scientific/medical fact before anyone else in the world – I kind of liked it. For me though, patient care and service always came first, not research and publishing scientific papers.

However, as far as I can determine, when it comes to writing medical/scientific papers, I am prolific compared to my fellow pathology residents who trained with me at Southeastern. I have not sent out questionnaires or investigated the matter thoroughly, but as far as I know, I have written more scientific/medical papers that have been published than all the rest of them combined.

Dr. Hollis trained practical, practicing pathologists, not researchers.

CHAPTER 64

During my time at Southeastern, Dr. Hollis was like a statue or a monument, solid and immutable. He won every teaching award there was to win.

So I was surprised when he left academic medicine to go into private practice. Dr. Eisen phoned me with the news.

"Why?" I asked.

"A bunch of kids in college, I suspect he needs the money."

A resident one year behind me at Southeastern, Jim Simpson, had gone into private practice at a small hospital in a suburb a little north of Atlanta. The suburb was growing like crazy, and the pathology workload was going up. Jim needed help, and Dr. Hollis needed money, so they teamed up. Dr. Hollis ended up with a well-paying job in a growing part of the country.

Southeastern held a farewell reception for Dr. Hollis, and I was invited, but I was unable to attend. A College of American Pathologists inspection of my lab was scheduled to happen the day following the event, and I just couldn't get away. Dr. Eisen called to try to get me to change my mind.

I said, "I don't think you need me there for you all to have a good time – it will be a fun party without me."

"It would be better if you were there," he said.

I hated to miss it.

CHAPTER 65

Of course Dr. Hollis was successful in his new job. Chad Sharon, my fellow resident, tennis player, and colleague at the Medical Examiner's Office, was now in private practice in Atlanta. He related to me the accolades Dr. Hollis was getting at his new job. At such events as tissue committee meetings and tumor board meetings, his clinical/pathology correlations and discussions were so erudite that he commonly got standing ovations.

Has that ever happened to me, or any other pathologist to my knowledge? No.

CHAPTER 66

A little after Dr. Hollis went into private practice, I yearned to reconnect with my friends and teachers from Southeastern. I decided to travel and attend Dr. Page's spring banquet at the Piedmont Club.

At the event I saw the residents who followed me carry on the Southeastern Pathology Department traditions. It was their turn to get a chair from Dr. Page inscribed *Audi Esse Verus*. I celebrated with them and got to see old friends. I had a good time.

Even though Dr. Hollis was no longer on the Southeastern faculty, he, like me, decided to attend the banquet. I talked to him. I was curious to learn how he liked private practice. In private practice the emphasis is on productivity and service, not teaching. I told him I thought he would miss the teaching. He said he really didn't, and that the medical staff at his small hospital was "a very inquisitive group."

He seemed happy.

CHAPTER 67

After my Southeastern training, I stayed at my first job three and a half years. Then I got a call from Doug Becker, who had been a couple of years ahead of me at Southeastern, and Don Esbenshade, who had been chief resident when I had started at Southeastern. They were in Atlanta with a pathology practice at Blue Stocking Hospital, a short distance north of the Southeastern campus. Their pathology volume was growing like crazy, a nice problem to have, but hectic. In addition, the third member of their group had left and taken another job, so on top of the growth they were experiencing, they were shorthanded. Doug and Don needed another pathologist to help them out. They needed me.

The job offer was generous and lucrative. I took the job. I returned to Atlanta and entered the milieu of Southeastern again, around doctors I had trained with, as well as my Southeastern professors.

Well, the Blue Stocking Hospital pathology practice was growing, all right. In fact, as far as I was concerned, it was growing too fast. I couldn't keep up. I was very uncomfortable handling large numbers of specimens, especially neuropathology specimens. In the three and a half years since I had left Southeastern, I had done no neuropathology because at my first job there was no neurosurgeon. In contrast, Blue Stocking Hospital prided itself on its neurosurgery department, promoting and advertising it as a "Center of Excellence," and it was. So all of a sudden I went from no neurosurgery specimens to a ton of neurosurgery specimens, and they weren't all straightforward cases – they were brain tumors, spinal cord tumors, and pediatric congenital malformations…tough cases.

Now I could take care of large numbers of specimens, and I could handle the neuropathology cases – I just couldn't do it fast. I worked long hours, and on weekends I also looked at slides, to try to keep up.

I'm not a quitter, but after six and a half months, I found another job. I turned in my resignation to Doug and Don. They weren't particularly sad to see me go. I moved to suburban Dallas, to join a suburban/rural practice of pathology, where I still work thirty-eight years later. I left Southeastern for good, slinking away with my tail between my legs, and nobody cared.

For the first time in my life I failed. I had done my best, but it wasn't good enough.

During my short stint at Blue Stocking Hospital, I was so busy that I did not get a chance to see much of the former residents and students I had trained with at Southeastern, or even to talk to them. I had not seen nor talked to Dr. Hollis.

The last few weeks before I left were eventful. I sent in an RSVP that I would attend Dr. Page's spring banquet at the Piedmont Club, and I was hoping to reconnect with everyone at the dinner, including Dr. Hollis. However, the evening of the event the operating rooms at Blue Stocking Hospital were so busy that one of us had to stay at the hospital and do the work and take care of what the operating rooms might need. That person was me. I didn't get home till 11 p.m., so I missed the banquet. I didn't see Dr. Hollis or anyone else.

A few days after the banquet, which was a few days before I moved away, I phoned Dr. Hollis at his office. I didn't want to leave town without at least some contact. I regretted the fact that I had missed his farewell reception at Southeastern a few years earlier, and that I hadn't seen or talked to him since I returned to Atlanta. I had something important to tell him: I tried not to be smarmy about it, but I told him how much I appreciated training under him, and how grateful I was for all he taught me.

I don't remember his reply exactly – something to the effect of like it was no big deal, or maybe something like…he really didn't give a shit. I really don't remember his exact response except that it was nothing smarmy at all, the direct opposite. I regarded his response as just fine.

Anyway, I do remember that Dr. Hollis *did* say he was disappointed he hadn't seen me since I returned, and that he was shocked that I had not attended Dr. Page's spring banquet. I told him why I missed the banquet. I also related to him that I was moving to take a new job, because things had not worked out at Blue Stocking Hospital.

"I'm not surprised," he said. "When you came back to work with Doug and Don, I was skeptical it would work, but no one asked me, so I kept my mouth shut."

That didn't make any sense to me. Of course I didn't ask Dr. Hollis about taking the job. I made my own choices. It wasn't like he was my mentor or anything. No one was.

CHAPTER 68

A few years later, Dr. Hollis failed as well, probably for the first time in his life. Jim Simpson fired him.

I found this out at Dr. Page's retirement banquet. I saw Dr. Hollis, but I did not get a chance to talk to him because the event was so crowded. The event was held at a large convention hall. Hundreds of former students, house staff, faculty, and dignitaries showed up to honor Dr. Page. Dr. Hollis was one of the speakers. I and all the other residents I trained with were amazed that Dr. Hollis could not only show up, but be a speaker – because his professional life was in shambles.

Dr. Simpson – Dr. Hollis's partner, former student, and former resident – fired Dr. Hollis because he had been having sex with one of his female administrative assistants, on hospital premises, during working hours. I don't know the details, whether they were caught in flagrante delicto, or if someone complained, but the end result was that Dr. Hollis was suddenly retired/fired.

This news was like an electric current overload through the grid of his former students and house staff, causing circuit breakers to trip and fuses to blow.

CHAPTER 69

Dr. Hollis continued to surprise everyone, not just his former residents and students, but his wife and family as well.

A few years after he was fired, the following happened: After lunch one day, a lunch fixed by his wife, Ellen, Dr. Hollis told his wife of several decades, the mother of his many children, that he was leaving and not coming back. He packed his bags, loaded them in his car, and moved out.

Then he drove over to the house of his administrative assistant lover and moved in with her and her young son. Dr. Hollis was the boy's father. The boy was now four years old and needed his dad. So Dr. Hollis showed up, divorced Ellen, married the mother of his newest son, and became a father to the boy.

For four years, the most important person in my life was Dr. Hollis. To this day, no one, with the exception of my parents, has had a bigger influence on my life. During my pathology training, he was a demigod, with an immutable premise: "You can't not know." How beguiling this commandment was for a young man like me. So I tried to live a heroic life like that, to be like Dr. Hollis. And I wasn't the only one. Southeastern was filled with students and pathology house staff just like me.

Thus, what a shock it was to me, to all of us, that Dr. Hollis was not a demigod, but a human – that he got hard and horny for a woman and screwed up, just like any other man, just like me. It shook me to my core. I thought he had all the answers. But it turned out he didn't have all the answers.

Or maybe, finally, he did.

CHAPTER 70

I talked to Dr. Hollis by phone one more time, after the turmoil in his life calmed down. I needed his expertise. I was asked by a neurologist to be a medical expert on a medical malpractice suit he was defending. The neurologist wanted me to review the autopsy findings, including the slides, pertaining to a patient of his who had died. The family of the deceased patient was suing him.

In my experience with medical malpractice suits, the whole case can turn on something totally unrelated to standard of care, or possible negligence, or anything having to do with the merits of the case. Instead, something completely unrelated to the merits of the case decides who wins and who loses, most often how sympathetic the plaintiff is.

This malpractice case, for some reason, was going to turn on the timing of some wounds the deceased had in his tongue. The tongue wounds were probably related to the patient's seizures. When these wounds occurred was going to be used to determine when the seizures had happened. In my opinion, the timing of these wounds and associated seizures was totally unrelated to the merits of the malpractice claim. Nevertheless, I had looked at the slides, and I was going to have to testify about when I thought these tongue wounds had happened. That wasn't easy to figure out, and the medical literature was not that helpful.

Of course, there was no person in the world better able to help me figure out the pathophysiology of the tongue injuries than Dr. Hollis. My plan was to describe the microscopic findings to him over the phone, and hopefully he could tell me how to interpret the findings, which was good enough for me. No one knew more about this stuff than Dr. Hollis.

He was hard to locate. This was still before the widespread use of the internet and cell phones. No one knew where Dr. Hollis was, or his phone number. Finally I phoned Dr. Page, who, even though he was retired, was still working part time at Southeastern.

I told Dr. Page what I needed. Initially, Dr. Page was reluctant to help me find Dr. Hollis, and suggested some newer members of the Southeastern faculty who could help me. About Dr. Hollis, Dr. Page said, "Darrell let his medical license expire. I begged him not to do it. At least keep your medical license, I told him, in case you need it someday, but he wouldn't listen. Darrell said, 'I'm done with medicine.'"

I wasn't interested in talking to anyone else about the tongue wounds. "With or without a medical license, there's only one Dr. Hollis," I said.

Dr. Page gave me Dr. Hollis's phone number. Dr. Page and I talked some more. Dr. Page told me that Dr. Hollis's present wife "is a good person. You would like her."

I phoned Dr. Hollis and asked him if I could discuss a specimen with him. "Shoot," he said. I described my observations of the pathologic findings and asked him questions. As expected, his answers and comments were very helpful. For one last time he was able to make everything make sense and come together.

After that business was concluded, we talked, just talked. When I told him I was now on the medical staffs at three competing hospitals in our community, he complimented me, saying that it spoke highly of me, that I must be doing an exemplary job to keep all three hospitals happy.

Dr. Hollis related to me that he had been in a skiing accident and suffered a brachial plexus injury, which caused some paralysis of one of his arms and some disability.

He also told me he had a young son whom he was helping to raise.

Dr. Hollis told me that he had left medicine and pathology, that it was time for the younger physicians and pathologists to take over, because so much had changed. "A lot of the new stuff is garbage, but some of it is good. It's time for me to move on and leave everything for the next generation."

He sounded in good spirits. It was a good call. It was the last time I talked to him.

CHAPTER 71

I have been to funerals where the minister used the metaphor that life is a journey, a journey that does not end with death. I think I have already covered death and dying in this book quite thoroughly, thank you very much for your support.

But I like the metaphor, so let me try to use it a little bit. In some ways my life *has* been a series of journeys.

For college, the metaphor I would use is a bus trip out West, full of adventure with canyons and mountains, highs and lows.

Medical school was exotic, a cruise in the South Pacific with majestic green mountains going into the clouds, and scuba diving with reefs and fish.

My residency at Southeastern was an Earthwatch mission to the Amazon jungle. It was interesting, but scary.

On each journey – college, medical school, and pathology residency at Southeastern – fellow travelers and I came together, worked together, and shared dreams. Then we moved on. The resulting humor and drama of such work is a story seldom told, although the movie *Broadcast News* did a good job of it. The movie artistically describes what occurs when three persons are thrown together at a workplace, a television news station, early in their careers, almost as if they were pathology residents in training. At the television news station the pressure and drama are intense, but their time together is actually relatively short. Then the three go their separate ways. It was like they were three ships passing each other in the night, the ships stopping for a short time while the passengers signaled to each other and rode tenders one ship to another; then the ships move on. A scene at the end of the movie shows them reunited but only briefly.

My life has been like that. The only friends from college I am in contact with are those I played with on the tennis team, and my get-togethers with them are brief and infrequent. I see my medical school classmates every five years at our reunions. That's it. The rest of the time we are engaged in our own medical practices, families, and communities.

I have not been invited to the Southeastern pathology banquet in decades. I doubt if it is even being held anymore. Dr. Page is deceased. Once in a while I run into one of my fellow Southeastern residents at a pathology meeting, but that happens fewer and fewer times as more of my colleagues retire. I did talk by phone recently to Chad Sharon, my former fellow resident, tennis partner, and colleague at the Medical Examiner's Office. Chad is still playing tennis and still practicing pathology in Atlanta at a private hospital near Southeastern. He told me that Dr. Hollis is teaching anatomy at a local dental school.

"Why?" I asked.

"He probably needs the money."

I disagreed. I doubted that he needed the money. Dr. Hollis needed the teaching. When Dr. Hollis told Dr. Page and me that he was "done with medicine," he did not say that he was done with teaching. As of the writing of this memoir, Dr. Hollis is in his nineties. I saw him recently on YouTube, still teaching, delivering a lecture about pathology. That's what he will be till the day he dies – a great teacher. As Chaucer says in *Canterbury Tales*: "And gladly would he learn and gladly teach."

CHAPTER 72

Let's face it: I couldn't handle having a mentor. I didn't want that kind of pressure.

Mack Puckett was my best friend in medical school and best man at my wedding. After he got out of the Navy, he did a urology residency at our Ivory Medical School. During his urology residency, he had a mentor, Dr. Ramsey, the chairman of the department. At the first five-year reunion of our class, I had dinner with Mack, Dr. Ramsey, and others in the urology program at a local restaurant. During the dinner, I listened to everyone, led by Dr. Ramsey, extol the extraordinary accomplishments of Mack. Dr. Ramsey said that Mack was further along at his level than any resident he ever had.

Later in the dinner, Mack whispered to me: "What we are doing here, Jack, is called the caring and feeding of the chief. Right now I am Dr. Ramsey's fair-haired boy, which is a very enviable position, but it is also a very dangerous position. I could fall very far, very fast."

That's too much pressure and responsibility for me.

See, had I a mentor, I would have had that kind of responsibility. I would have been required to live up to someone else's standards, in addition to the standards I set for myself already. I never wanted that kind of responsibility, that kind of ambiguity. I don't think I could have handled it. Life for me was hard enough without those complications.

Mack didn't write a book about his mentor. I am not aware of any physician who has written about his or her mentor. Sadly, doctors tend to restrict their reading and writing to medical texts and articles, with the resultant loss of imagination and creativity. It makes me weep.

Nevertheless, I wish to explore the mentor-pupil relationship, even if I must look to other fields of endeavor for such knowledge. Let's try the art of writing. It may be a leap to try to connect pathology, medicine, and writing with the mentor-pupil relationship, but it's worth a try. After all, this is a book, and I am supposed to be a writer. Maybe there are stories in the literature that can educate us about the subject.

Such stories are not hard to find. They tend to be very literate and illustrative of the pupil-mentor relationship. However, my understanding of the tales is that they tell some of the dangers of such a relationship, regardless of the field – pathology, medicine, writing…or anything else.

For example, I recently read Paul Theroux's memoir *Sir Vidia's Shadow: A Friendship across Five Continents*, in which he describes how his mentor, V. S. Naipaul, encouraged his writing career. One of the things that makes the book interesting is the high-profile falling-out the two had at the end, which for a while was the talk of the literary world. The relationship between the two ended when V. S. Naipaul remarried after the death of his first wife. The mentor-pupil relationship didn't survive the new marriage – a sad ending.

Another good story is the appropriately titled *Mentor: A Memoir* by Tom Grimes, a justly praised book about the author and his relationship with Frank Conroy, best known for his great memoir *Stop-Time*. The heart of the book describes the time Grimes spent at the Iowa Writers Workshop when Conroy was the director of the program. It's an eloquent, moving, heartfelt story, and I'm sure Frank Conroy helped Tom Grimes's career. However, reading between the lines, I think it's plausible that there was a downside for Mr. Grimes to have such a strong mentor, for these reasons:

1. Mr. Conroy loved the submission by Tom Grimes when he applied to get into the Iowa writing school, raving about it to anyone who would listen. Not surprisingly, this did not endear Grimes to the other aspiring writers in the class. So Grimes was pretty much cut off from any input or teaching from his classmates. At Southeastern such a development would have been fatal to my training, because I got much of my education from my fellow residents.

2. Having Mr. Conroy as a mentor stunted Grimes's initiative. As Tom Grimes was writing his book *A Stone of the Heart*, he was writing for one reader, and one reader only – Frank Conroy. If Mr. Conroy liked the writing, it stayed in the book; if he didn't, it went into the wastebasket. Tom Grimes was oblivious to the comments of others. I think this was probably an error. Perhaps Tom Grimes would have done better if he worked on his own or relied on other readers in addition to Conroy.

3. *Stone of the Heart*, in Tom Grimes's assessment, was in some ways a failure. Mr. Conroy loved it, but other readers, not so much. Bids from publishers were not as lucrative as Grimes and Conroy hoped, and both were disappointed in the number of books sold.

I could be wrong, but I regard this story as somewhat of a cautionary tale.

Back to medicine.

John McCurdie was a classmate and good friend of mine during my time at Ivory Medical School. When he graduated, he decided to go into pathology, just as I did. Unlike me, however, John was encouraged in this course of action by Dr. Bruce Woolridge, who was in charge of our second-year pathology course. Dr. Woolridge was also a world-famous hematopathologist. Dr. Woolridge became a mentor to John, who went on to become as much like Dr. Woolridge as was humanly possible. Like Dr. Woolridge, John became a hematopathologist, and when Dr. Woolridge decided he no longer wanted to be in charge of the second-year pathology course, well, John decided he would do that too.

Strange then, decades later when Dr. Woolridge retired, I attended his retirement party but John did not. He was nowhere to be seen. I thought there must have been something pretty important going on that day in John's life to make him miss the retirement festivities. Strange.

A few years later, Dr. Woolridge died, and John did not attend the funeral or reception. I was there, but John was not. Strange, very strange.

Recently I attended the reunion of our Ivory Medical School class, and John was there. I asked him if there had been a falling-out between him and Dr. Woolridge.

"Did something happen?" I asked.

John laughed bitterly. "Why would you ask that, Jack!?"

I shook my head and said, "I really don't know."

This is what John said:

"For a very long time, Dr. Woolridge was a great mentor, a fantastic mentor, but he stayed around too long. He lost his game, didn't know when to quit. The hematopathology department started to go downhill. The final straw was when he decided he was going to hire a certain pathologist, who will go unnamed, who was totally unqualified to join our department. I was the one delegated to go into Dr. Woolridge's office and tell Dr. Woolridge that the decision of the department was that his person would not be hired. That was the end of our relationship. He never forgave me for what he regarded as treacherous backstabbing behavior. He never talked to me again."

I couldn't live that way, walking on eggshells, censoring what I say or do. I have to live my own way and kill my own snakes.

One other thing. I wasn't smart enough to have Dr. Hollis as a mentor. Not even close.

I could only be me, and no one wanted to be a mentor to that.

CHAPTER 73

I suspect in every person's life, there is a certain period of time that has influences way out of proportion to the time frame. For some, it may be time in the armed forces, especially during war. For others it may be time in high school; the best example I know is a fictional one – Harry "Rabbit" Angstrom, the protagonist of the great Rabbit saga books by John Updike: the high point of Rabbit's life by far was his high school years when he was a basketball star. For others it may be time in college, maybe as part of a fraternity or sorority where friendships were made that last a lifetime.

For me that period of time was my Southeastern pathology residency. It lasted only four years, which in the overall span of my life is a very small percentage. But those were pivotal years, in some ways the most important years of my life when I was trained in my life's work, when I discovered my purpose in life – to take care of patients using my pathology skills and perform that function as well as possible. Dr. Hollis with his commandment "you can't not know" found a dedicated disciple.

Then I was a young man. Now I am an old man, and I know that his precept is wrong. In fact, I *can* not know.

So why did Dr. Hollis mislead me? Why did he set a standard that he had to have known was unattainable, even counterproductive? Sometimes a pathologist, or any physician, really does not know the correct diagnosis or treatment. If the physician or pathologist then proceeds as if he does know the answers, and really doesn't – the results can be catastrophic – an incorrect diagnosis and/or the wrong treatment.

Perhaps his statement "you can't not know" was made tongue in cheek. This is possible. Dr. Hollis was a consummate actor. I eventually figured out that he could be conducting an autopsy review and on the outside be trembling with rage at some miscreant pathology resident, while on the inside he was planning how he could finish up and get to his afternoon touch football game as quickly as possible.

But I don't think he was acting. I think Dr. Hollis gave us the premise of "you can't not know" as a step on the road to wisdom, not a final destination.

And the road to wisdom has steps along the way, which can't be skipped. There are no shortcuts.

Take winning. When I was young, I was a competitor, a hothead. Winning was the most important thing to me – tennis tournaments, wrestling matches, debate trophies. I had to get the best grades in my premed courses in college, *had* to. I was driven. I had to be a winner. I divided people into winners or losers, one or the other, and I had to be in the winning camp.

I don't think that way anymore, haven't for a long time. I don't think winning is very important anymore. Kindness is.

But here's the thing, to have that attitude now, I had to go through a phase when I had some wins – won some tennis tournaments, won some wrestling matches, garnered a debate trophy or two, gained acceptance into medical school, graduated from medical school, and completed a pathology residency at Southeastern. At those points in my life, I did have to care about winning, and win, because they were steps that couldn't be skipped before I could go on learning.

Similarly, I had to go through a period when my philosophy was "you can't not know" to get to the other side, and know that I could not know – that I didn't have to know everything about medicine, pathology, or anything else. No one can know it all, and no one has all the answers, including Dr. Hollis. Still, to try to follow the motto "you can't not know" was a step Dr. Hollis wanted me to take, wanted all of his students to take, because for a pathologist/physician in training, his motto was a good motto. It made me strive to learn as much as I possibly could at that time of my life, when I was learning to be a physician/pathologist. It was a step in my life that I could not skip.

But pathology, medicine, and life are full of ambiguity, things that I don't know and will never know. I think part of maturity and wisdom is to know that I can't know it all, that I have to live with ignorance about certain things, and I have to do the best I can and live in peace. We all do.

And here's the crazy thing – that includes Dr. Hollis. I have no doubt that Dr. Hollis knew what he presented as an immutable premise was false. Not only did he know the grammar was bad, but as a philosophical guide it was unworkable, in pathology and in life. Yet he preached this to us, his residents and his students, and ostensibly applied it to himself.

But he really didn't. He couldn't. No one can. The *true meaning* of his credo "you can't not know" is the direct opposite, which of course, he knew the whole time. He waited for us to figure it out and join him.

That is his legacy.

CHAPTER 74

Nowadays, the only time I see Southeastern is from the air, as I fly over it on trips I take. Some of the trips I take are medical in nature, going to meetings of the College of American Pathologists (CAP) or the American Society of Clinical Pathology (ASCP), or to do laboratory inspections, or to take courses on various subjects to improve my skills. I also take trips for pleasure that I had to defer when I was in training – when I didn't have the time or the money. Well, I still don't have much time, but I do have some money.

Therefore, I travel a lot and fly on airplanes a lot. Southeastern is located in Atlanta, the city with the busiest airport in the world, a major hub. Sometimes when I travel, there is a brief layover in the Atlanta Airport, where I catch connecting flights. As I fly over Southeastern, I usually have an out-of-body experience, which goes like this:

It's late morning or early afternoon, and the plane reaches the airspace overlying the Southeastern campus, which is nestled in the city, near the airport. The plane circles the sky, waiting to land, and I catch a glimpse of Southeastern. The plane lands, and after a brief layover, I get on another plane and it takes off. As we gain altitude, I sit in my window seat and look down and see the Southeastern campus, the shiny buildings reflecting the sunlight – the architecture so recognizable that I easily make out the Pathology Department with its conference rooms, offices, and laboratories. I remember my time there and wonder, just wonder. I go into a trance, a vision, and I see the young interns and residents continuing the traditions of medicine and pathology, learning, and then I see Dr. Hollis teaching these young interns and residents who have taken my place, and I note how they are busting their butts to be good pathologists, and then for a few minutes I not only see them, but I am *with* them, learning from Dr. Hollis once again, along with Layne and Fred and Sid – there is a sense of not only *seeing* Southeastern again, but *being* Southeastern again. But yet, yet, I'm not part of it anymore, because my time there has passed, and I have to make way for a new set of interns and residents, so I have to leave, and so does Dr. Hollis. Of course, what I am describing is not real, but wait, somehow seeing Southeastern, the place where such an important part of my life took place, makes the memory real, makes everything real, like it really did happen, and it really is happening, and for a short time, once again I am that idealistic young man starting out my life's work, and I see that young man, myself, as I was, and I can, however briefly, *be* that young man again, living the most intense period of my life.

Then the plane turns and banks to go in a different direction, toward my final destination. Southeastern, Dr. Hollis, and that young man fade in the distance, replaced by a curtain of clouds.

Book Jacket

This second book in the Jack Spenser, M.D., series describes the years of training it takes to become a physician/pathologist. The story focuses on the complex relationship between an apprentice and master whose credo is "You can't not know." Jack's struggle to meet such a high standard results in a compelling story with highs, lows, success, failure, and ultimately wisdom. In addition, some parts of the book are really funny.

About the Author

Dr. Spenser is a practicing physician who has written several scientific articles published in various medical journals. This is his second book.

Also By Jack Spenser, M.D.

Diary of a Malpractice Lawsuit: A Physician's Journey and Survival Guide

Made in the USA
Middletown, DE
07 November 2020

23486437R00116